THE BEST OF IRELAND CHORD SONGBOOK

Published by
Wise Publications
14-15 Berners Street, London W1T 3LJ, United Kingdom.

Exclusive distributors:
Music Sales Limited
Distribution Centre,
Newmarket Road, Bury St Edmunds, Suffolk, IP33 3YB, United Kingdom.
Music Sales Pty Limited
20 Resolution Drive, Caringbah, NSW 2229, Australia.

Order No. AM996160
ISBN 978-1-84772-861-6

Compiled by Nick Crispin.
Edited by Adrian Hopkins.
Music arranged by Matt Cowe.
Music processed by Paul Ewers Music Design.
Cover designed by Michael Bell Design.
Cover flag image courtesy of Argus/Fotolia .

Printed in the EU.

www.musicsales.com

WISE PUBLICATIONS
part of The Music Sales Group
London / New York / Paris / Sydney / Copenhagen / Berlin / Madrid / Tokyo

Relative Tuning

The guitar can be tuned with the aid of pitch pipes or dedicated electronic guitar tuners which are available through your local music dealer. If you do not have a tuning device, you can use relative tuning. Estimate the pitch of the 6th string as near as possible to E or at least a comfortable pitch (not too high, as you might break other strings in tuning up). Then, while checking the various positions on the diagram, place a finger from your left hand on the:

5th fret of the E or 6th string and **tune the open A** (or 5th string) to the note (A)

5th fret of the A or 5th string and **tune the open D** (or 4th string) to the note (D)

5th fret of the D or 4th string and **tune the open G** (or 3rd string) to the note (G)

4th fret of the G or 3rd string and **tune the open B** (or 2nd string) to the note (B)

5th fret of the B or 2nd string and **tune the open E** (or 1st string) to the note (E)

E or 6th | A or 5th | D or 4th | G or 3rd | B or 2nd | E or 1st

Head

Nut

1st Fret

2nd Fret

3rd Fret

4th Fret (B)

5th Fret (A) (D) (G) (E)

Reading Chord Boxes

Chord boxes are diagrams of the guitar neck viewed head upwards, face on as illustrated. The top horizontal line is the nut, unless a higher fret number is indicated, the others are the frets.

The vertical lines are the strings, starting from E (or 6th) on the left to E (or 1st) on the right.

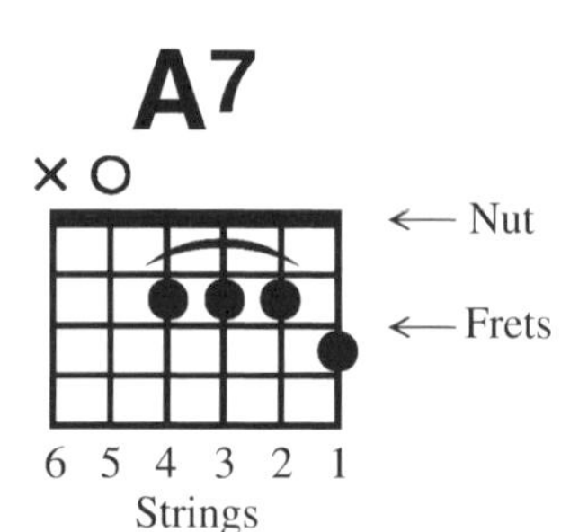

The black dots indicate where to place your fingers.

Strings marked with an O are played open, not fretted. Strings marked with an X should not be played.

The curved bracket indicates a 'barre' - hold down the strings under the bracket with your first finger, using your other fingers to fret the remaining notes.

All I Want Is You

Words & Music by U2

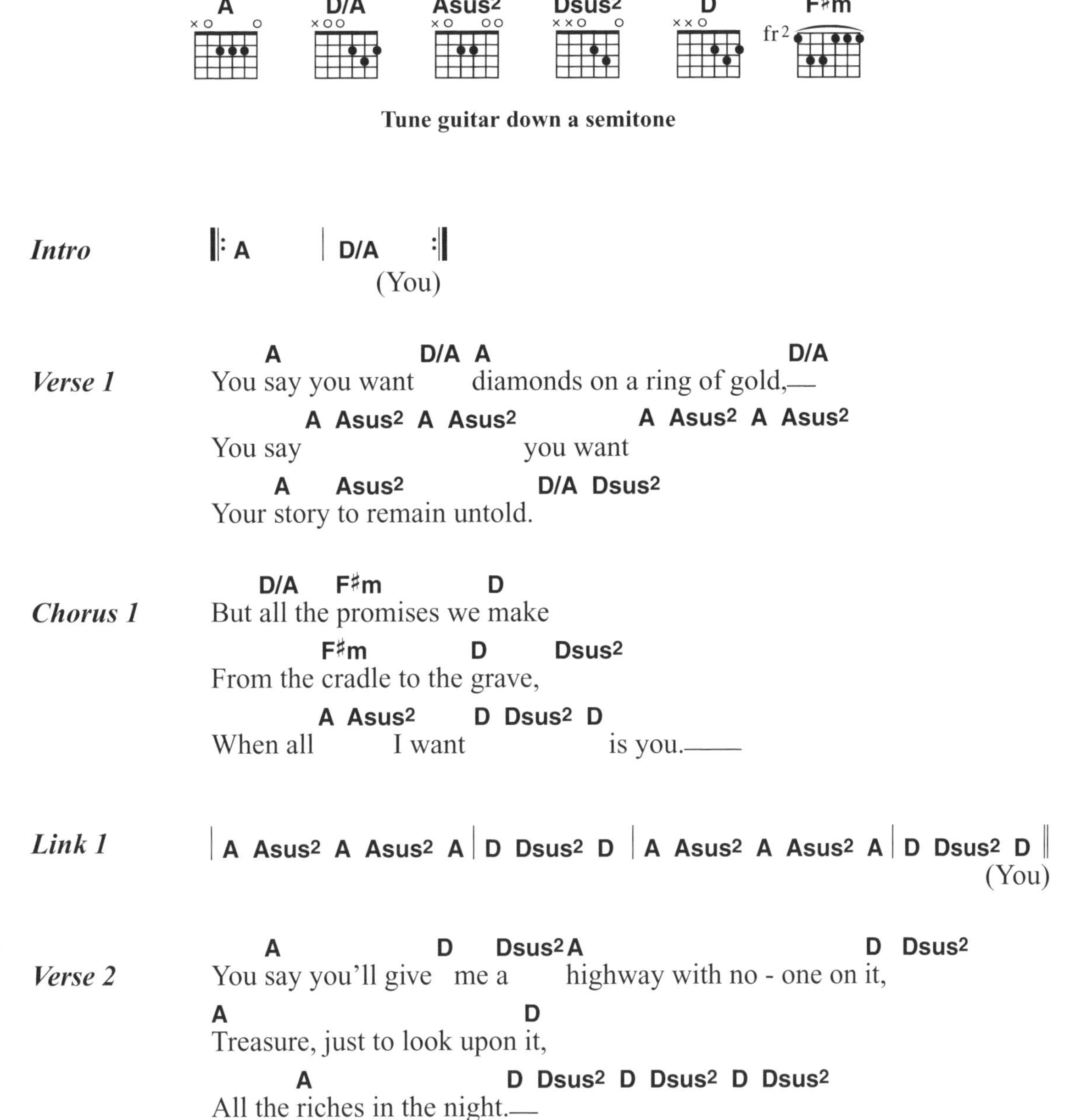

Tune guitar down a semitone

Intro ‖: A | D/A :‖
(You)

Verse 1

A D/A A D/A
You say you want diamonds on a ring of gold,—

A Asus2 A Asus2 A Asus2 A Asus2
You say you want

A Asus2 D/A Dsus2
Your story to remain untold.

Chorus 1

D/A F♯m D
But all the promises we make

F♯m D Dsus2
From the cradle to the grave,

A Asus2 D Dsus2 D
When all I want is you.——

Link 1 | A Asus2 A Asus2 A | D Dsus2 D | A Asus2 A Asus2 A | D Dsus2 D ‖
(You)

Verse 2

A D Dsus2 A D Dsus2
You say you'll give me a highway with no - one on it,

A D
Treasure, just to look upon it,

A D Dsus2 D Dsus2 D Dsus2
All the riches in the night.—

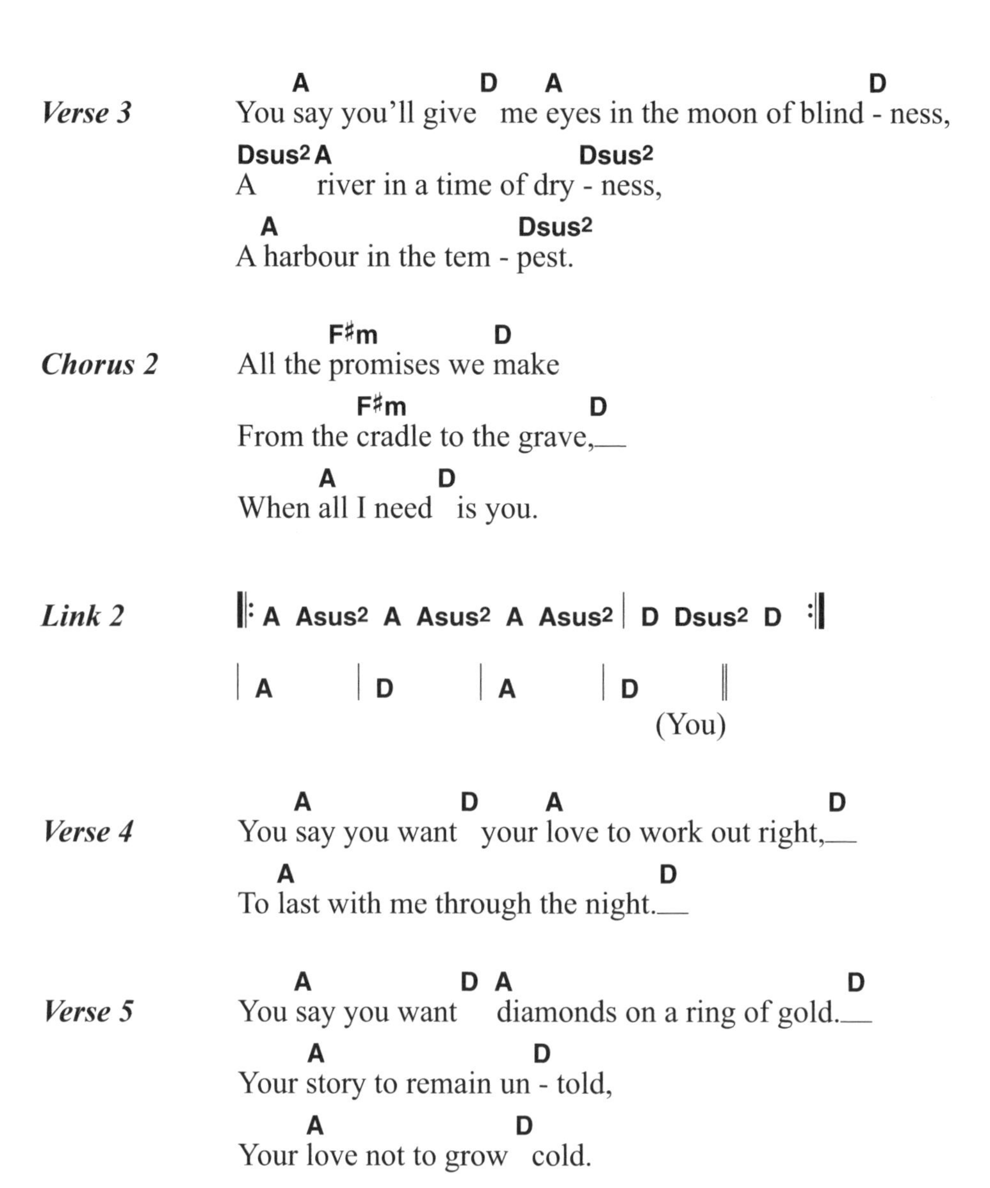
Verse 3
A D A D
You say you'll give me eyes in the moon of blind - ness,
Dsus2 A Dsus2
A river in a time of dry - ness,
A Dsus2
A harbour in the tem - pest.
Chorus 2
F♯m D
All the promises we make
F♯m D
From the cradle to the grave,
A D
When all I need is you.
Link 2
A Asus2 A Asus2 A Asus2 D Dsus2 D
A D A D
(You)
Verse 4
A D A D
You say you want your love to work out right,
A D
To last with me through the night.
Verse 5
A D A D
You say you want diamonds on a ring of gold.
A D
Your story to remain un - told,
A D
Your love not to grow cold.

Chorus 3

```
       F♯m          D
All the promises we break
          F♯m                  D
From the cradle to the grave,—
        A         D
When all I want   is you.
```

Link 3

```
‖: A  Asus2  A  Asus2  A  Asus2 | D  Dsus2  :‖ Play 4 times
```

Interlude

```
    A  Asus2  A  Asus2  A  Asus2  D  Dsus2
‖: You,————————                   all I want is—  :‖ Play 3 times
A  Asus2  A  Asus2  A  Asus2  D  Dsus2
You.———————————————————
```

Instrumental

```
‖: A  Asus2  A  Asus2  A  Asus2 | D  Dsus2  :‖ Play 8 times

| A         | D        ‖

‖: A  Asus2 | D        :‖ Play 5 times
```

Outro

```
‖: A       | D       | A       | D       :‖ Repeat to fade
```

After All

Words & Music by Paul Linehan, Niall Linehan & Ashley Keating

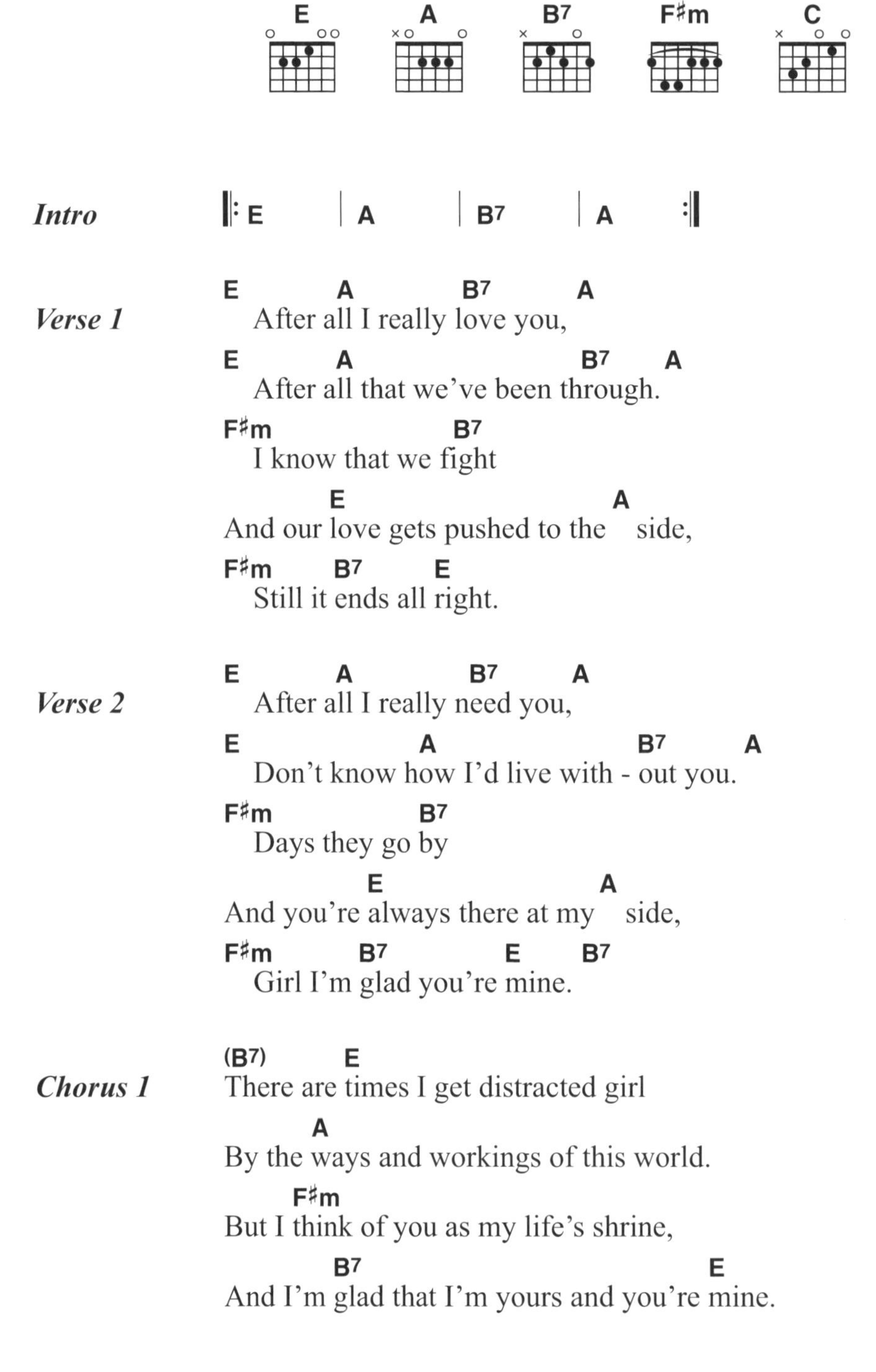

Intro

|: E | A | B7 | A :|

Verse 1

```
E           A              B7          A
   After all I really love you,
E           A                         B7       A
   After all that we've been through.
F♯m                   B7
   I know that we fight
              E                              A
And our love gets pushed to the    side,
F♯m        B7        E
   Still it ends all right.
```

Verse 2

```
E           A              B7          A
   After all I really need you,
E                A                        B7          A
   Don't know how I'd live with - out you.
F♯m                B7
   Days they go by
                 E                           A
And you're always there at my    side,
F♯m          B7                 E        B7
   Girl I'm glad you're mine.
```

Chorus 1

```
(B7)        E
There are times I get distracted girl
          A
By the ways and workings of this world.
        F♯m
But I think of you as my life's shrine,
             B7                              E
And I'm glad that I'm yours and you're mine.
```

```
           E              A                 B7   A
Verse 3       When I'm far from home and lonely,
           E          A            B7  A
              And I think about my life.
           F♯m          B7
              I think about you,
                E              A
           All the little things that you do
           F♯m        B7         E     B7
              And I'm glad you're mine.

           (B7)     E
Chorus 2   There are times I get distracted girl
                 A
           By the ways and workings of this world.
               F♯m
           But I think of you as my life's shrine,
                  B7                         A      E  A  B7
           And I'm glad that I'm yours and you're mine.________

           (B7)    E
Bridge     Ba, da, da, ba, da, da, ba, ba, ba.
                   A
           Ba, da, da, ba, da, da, ba, ba, ba.
                   F♯m
           Ba, da, da, ba, da, da, ba, ba, ba.

           (F♯m)   E
Outro      Ba, da, da, ba, da, da, ba, ba, ba.
                   A
           Ba, da, da, ba, da, da, ba, ba, ba.
                   F♯m
           Ba, da, da, ba, da, da, ba, ba, ba.
                   B7                    E
           And I'm glad that after all you're mine.

           Ba, da, da, ba, da, da, ba, ba, ba.
                   A
           Ba, da, da, ba, da, da, ba, ba, ba.
                   F♯m
           Ba, da, da, ba, da, da, ba, ba, ba.
                   B7                    C    E
           And I'm glad that after all you're mine.
```

Alone Again (Naturally)

Words & Music by Gilbert O'Sullivan

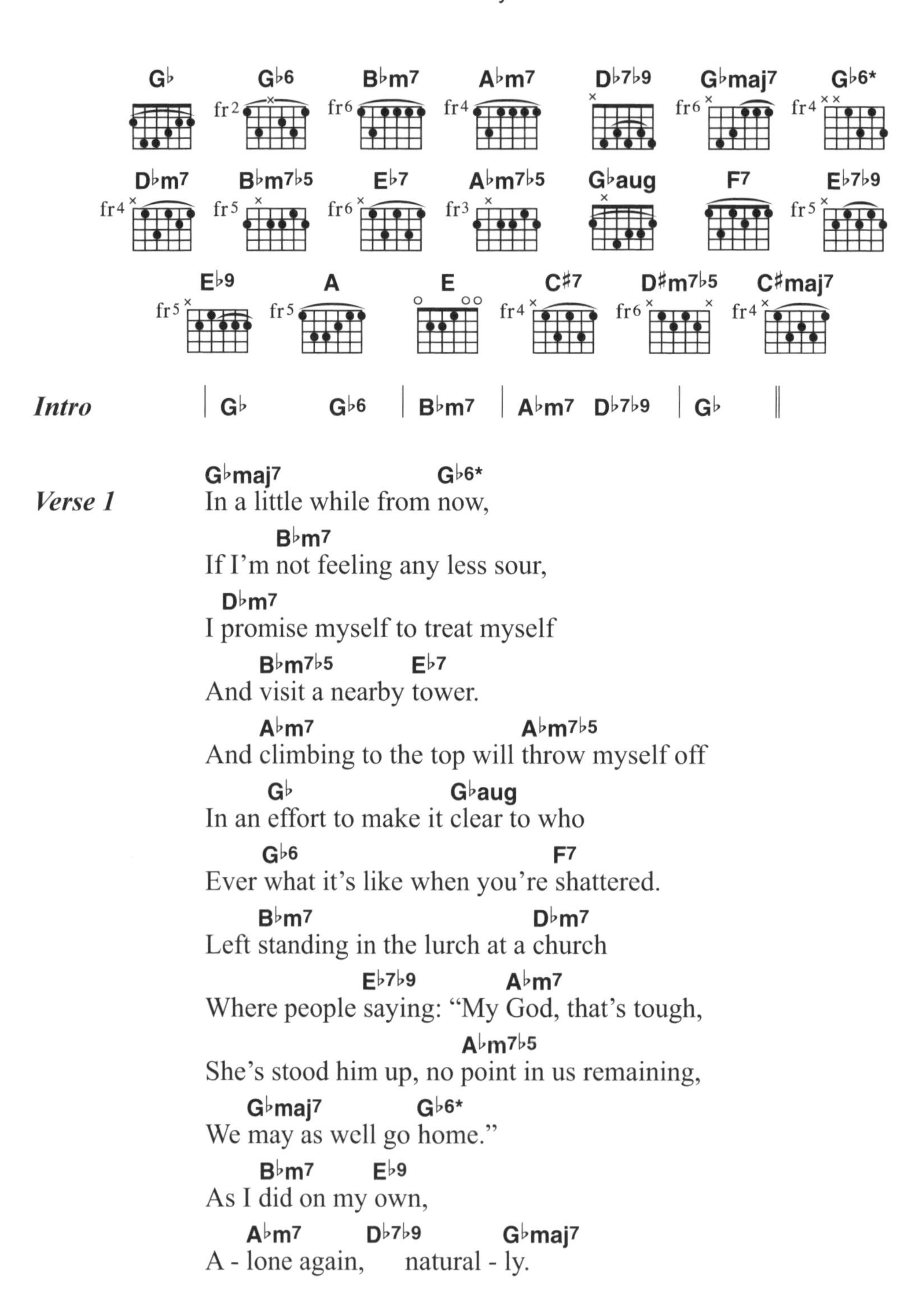

Verse 2

G♭maj7   G♭6*
To think that only yester - day
     B♭m7
I was cheerful, bright and gay.
        D♭m7
Looking forward to, well who wouldn't do,
    B♭m7♭5   E♭7♭9
The role I was about to play.
      A♭m7   A♭m7♭5
But as if to knock me down, re - ality came around,
          G♭   G♭aug
And with - out so much, as a mere touch
       G♭6   F7
Cut me into little pieces.
B♭m7
Leaving me to doubt,
       D♭m7   E♭7♭9
Talk a - bout God and His mercy,
  A♭m7
Or if He really does exist,
A♭m7♭5   G♭maj7   G♭6*
Why did He desert me   in my hour of need.
 B♭m7   E♭9
I truly am in - deed
  A♭m7   D♭7♭9   G♭maj7
A - lone again,   natural - ly.

Bridge

  A
It seems to me that there are more hearts
E   A♭m7♭5
Broken in the world that can't be mended
C♯7   A
  Left unat - tended.
D♯m7♭5   C♯maj7
  What do we do?
         A♭m7 D♭7
What do we do?

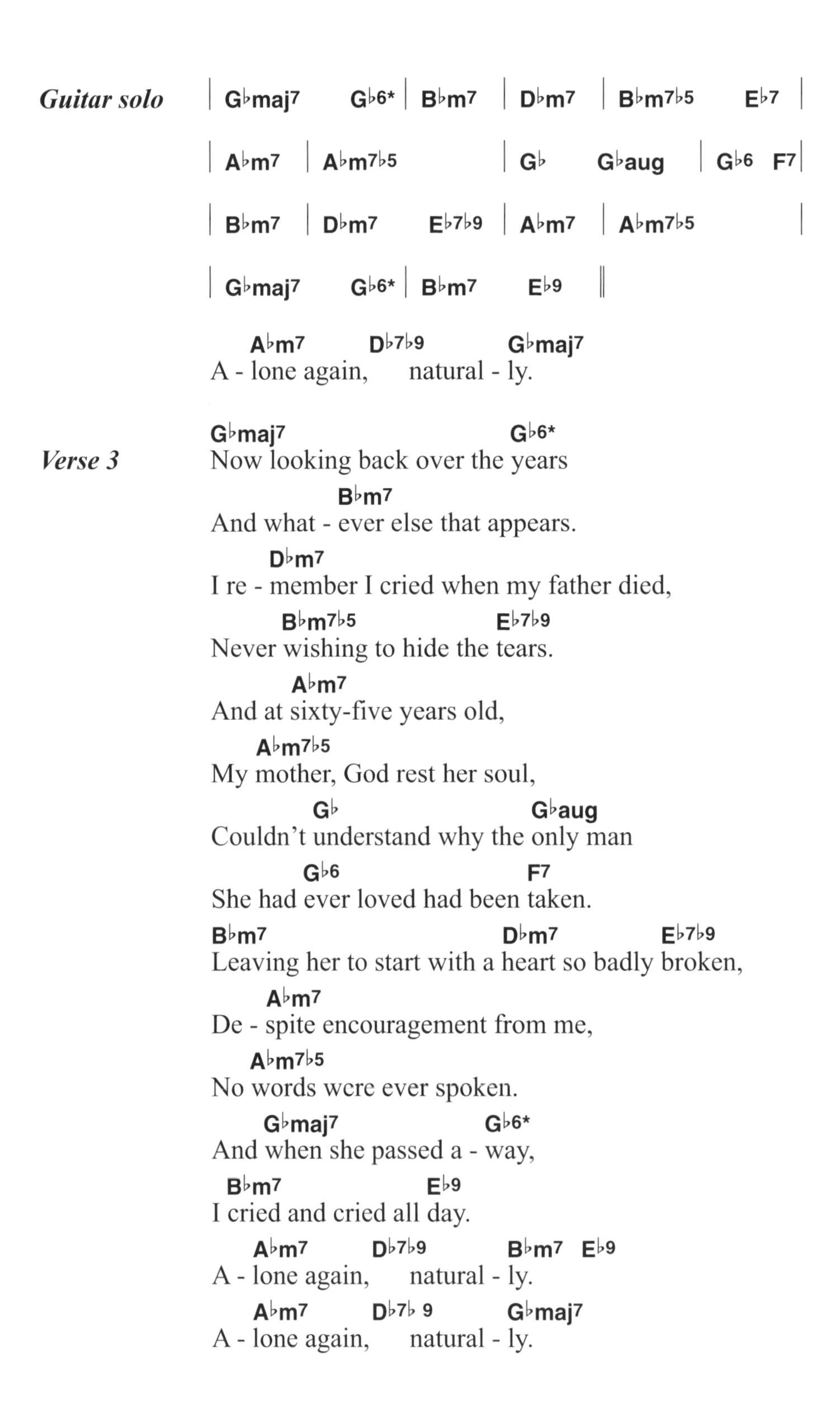
Guitar solo
G♭maj7 G♭6*	B♭m7	D♭m7	B♭m7♭5 E♭7
A♭m7	A♭m7♭5	G♭ G♭aug	G♭6 F7
B♭m7	D♭m7 E♭7♭9	A♭m7	A♭m7♭5
G♭maj7 G♭6*	B♭m7 E♭9	
A♭m7 D♭7♭9 G♭maj7
A - lone again, natural - ly.
Verse 3
G♭maj7 G♭6*
Now looking back over the years
B♭m7
And what - ever else that appears.
D♭m7
I re - member I cried when my father died,
B♭m7♭5 E♭7♭9
Never wishing to hide the tears.
A♭m7
And at sixty-five years old,
A♭m7♭5
My mother, God rest her soul,
G♭ G♭aug
Couldn’t understand why the only man
G♭6 F7
She had ever loved had been taken.
B♭m7 D♭m7 E♭7♭9
Leaving her to start with a heart so badly broken,
A♭m7
De - spite encouragement from me,
A♭m7♭5
No words were ever spoken.
G♭maj7 G♭6*
And when she passed a - way,
B♭m7 E♭9
I cried and cried all day.
A♭m7 D♭7♭9 B♭m7 E♭9
A - lone again, natural - ly.
A♭m7 D♭7♭ 9 G♭maj7
A - lone again, natural - ly.

Alternative Ulster

Words & Music by Jake Burns & Gordon Ogilvie

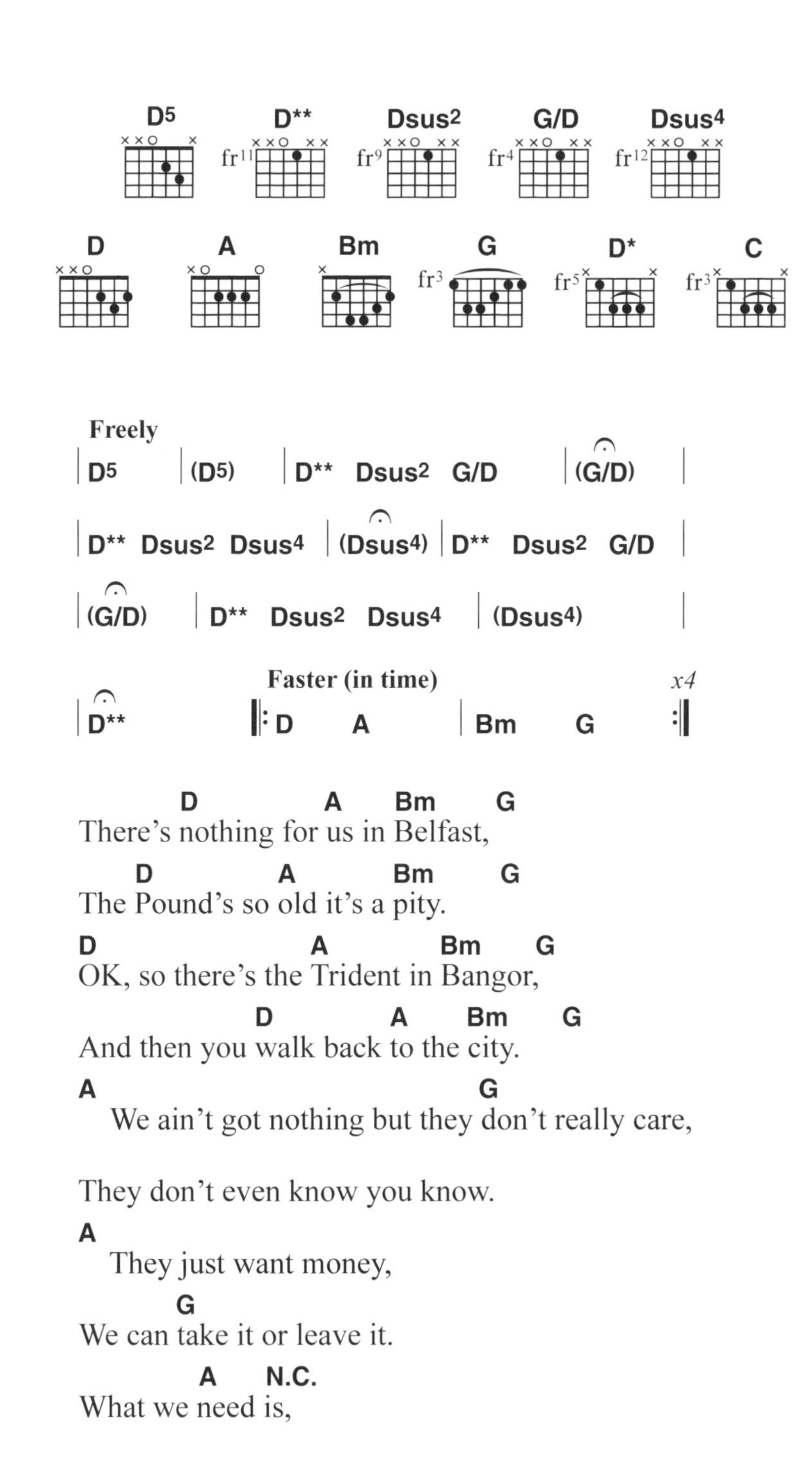

Intro

Freely

D5	(D5)	D** Dsus2 G/D	(G/D)
D** Dsus2 Dsus4	(Dsus4)	D** Dsus2 G/D
(G/D)	D** Dsus2 Dsus4	(Dsus4)

Faster (in time) *x4*

| D** ||: D A | Bm G :||

Verse 1

```
             D           A     Bm      G
There's nothing for us in Belfast,
         D        A        Bm       G
The Pound's so old it's a pity.
D                   A          Bm     G
OK, so there's the Trident in Bangor,
                  D        A     Bm      G
And then you walk back to the city.
A                              G
   We ain't got nothing but they don't really care,

They don't even know you know.
A
   They just want money,
          G
We can take it or leave it.
           A     N.C.
What we need is,
```

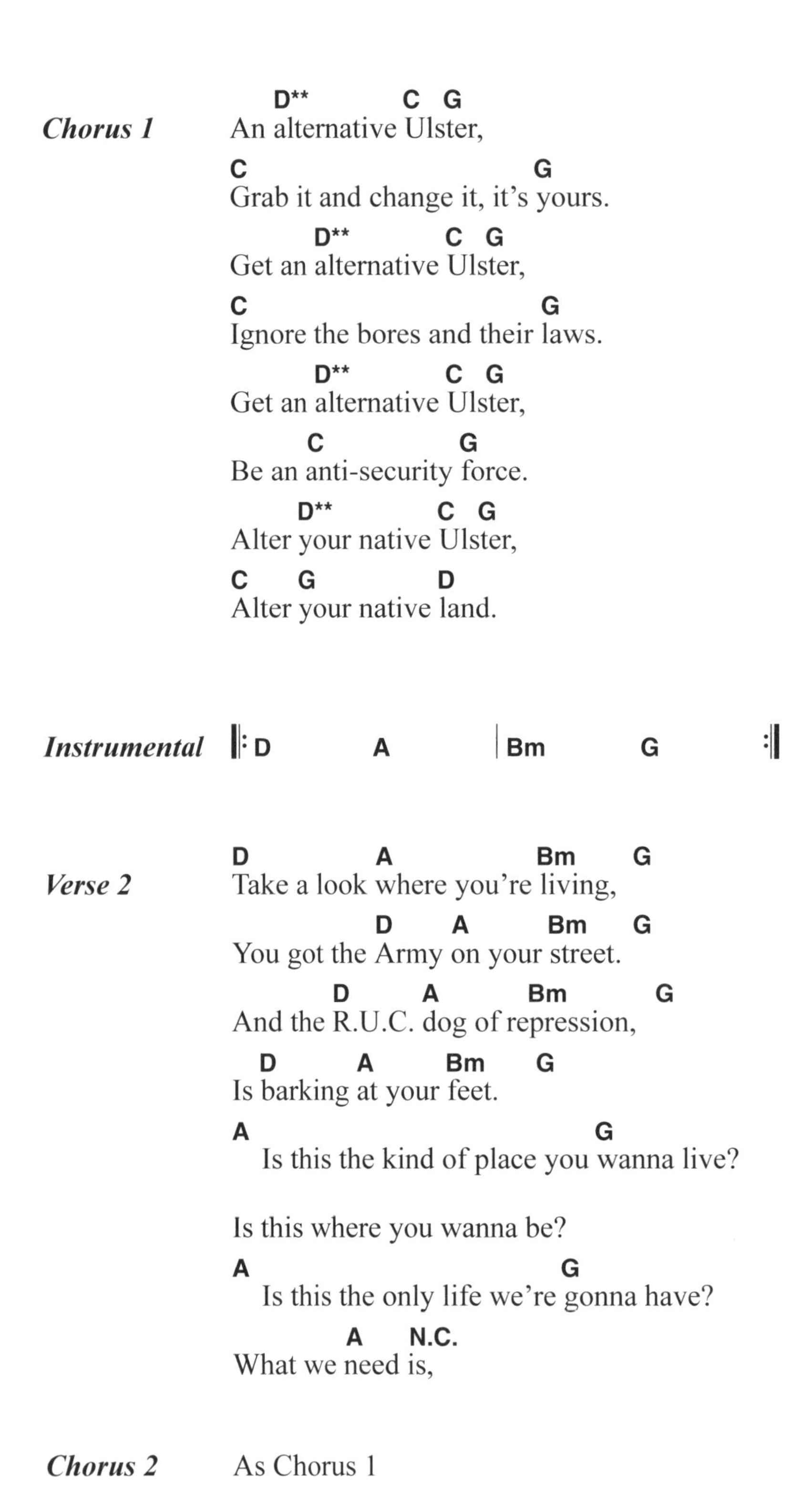

```
Chorus 1        D**          C   G
                An alternative Ulster,
                C                          G
                Grab it and change it, it's yours.
                       D**          C   G
                Get an alternative Ulster,
                C                           G
                Ignore the bores and their laws.
                       D**          C   G
                Get an alternative Ulster,
                       C              G
                Be an anti-security force.
                     D**           C   G
                Alter your native Ulster,
                C     G           D
                Alter your native land.


Instrumental    |: D          A          | Bm          G          :|


                D          A              Bm      G
Verse 2         Take a look where you're living,
                           D    A       Bm     G
                You got the Army on your street.
                         D      A        Bm          G
                And the R.U.C. dog of repression,
                  D       A       Bm      G
                Is barking at your feet.
                A                                G
                   Is this the kind of place you wanna live?

                Is this where you wanna be?
                A                              G
                   Is this the only life we're gonna have?
                            A     N.C.
                What we need is,


Chorus 2        As Chorus 1
```

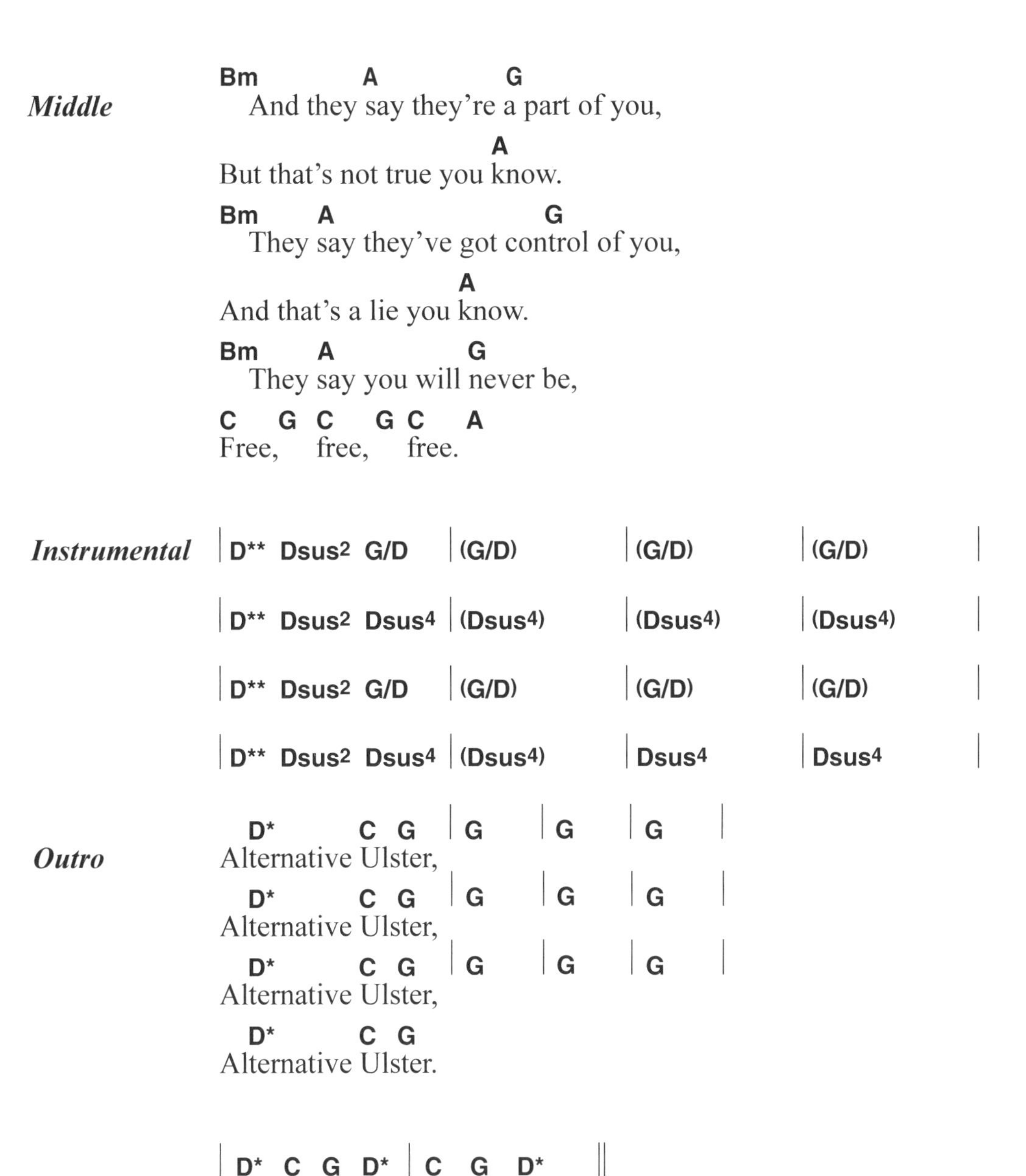

Middle

Bm A G
And they say they're a part of you,
A
But that's not true you know.
Bm A G
They say they've got control of you,
A
And that's a lie you know.
Bm A G
They say you will never be,
C G C G C A
Free, free, free.

Instrumental

D** Dsus2 G/D	(G/D)	(G/D)	(G/D)
D** Dsus2 Dsus4	(Dsus4)	(Dsus4)	(Dsus4)
D** Dsus2 G/D	(G/D)	(G/D)	(G/D)
D** Dsus2 Dsus4	(Dsus4)	Dsus4	Dsus4

Outro

D* C G | G | G | G |
Alternative Ulster,
D* C G | G | G | G |
Alternative Ulster,
D* C G | G | G | G |
Alternative Ulster,
D* C G
Alternative Ulster.

| D* C G D* | C G D* ||

Big Sur

Words by Conor Deasy
Music by Conor Deasy, Kevin Horan, Pádraic McMahon, Daniel Ryan & Ben Carrigan
Contains elements from "Theme From The Monkees" –
Words & Music by Tommy Boyce & Bobby Hart

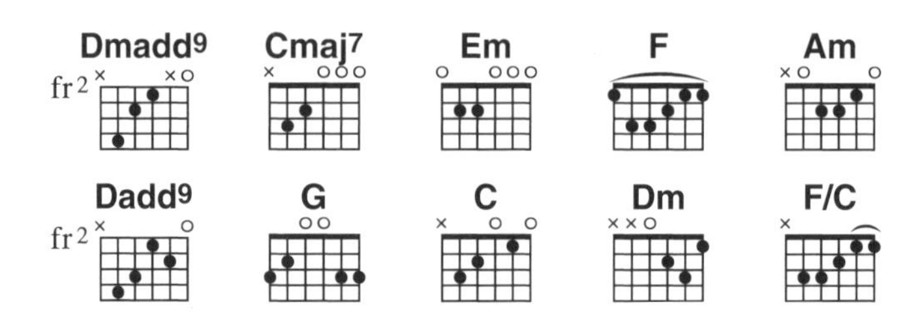

Intro | Dmadd9 | Cmaj7 | Dmadd9 | Cmaj7 Em ||

Verse 1

```
F                    Am
   So much for the city
Dadd9
Tell me that you'll dance to the end,
     F                                  G   Am
Just tell me that you'll dance to the end.
F                      Am
   Hey, hey you're the Monkees,
    Dadd9
And people said you monkeyed around,
    F                        G  Am
But nobody's listening now.
```

Chorus 1

```
C             F          Dm      G
   Just don't go back to Big Sur,
Em            F
   Hangin' a - round,
Em                       F
   Lettin' your old man down.
C             F          Dm
   Just don't go back to Big Sur,
G                        F/C
Baby, baby, please don't go,
    G                        C      Em
Oh, baby, baby, please don't go.
```

Verse 2

```
F                       Am
   So much for the street lights,
          Dadd9
They're never gonna guide you home,
     F                                        G   Am
No, they're never gonna guide you home.
F                               Am
   Down at the steamboat show, yeah,
Dadd9
All the kids start spitting,
                  F                       G  Am
I guess I didn't live up to the billing.
```

Chorus 2

```
C               F            Dm       G
   Just don't go back to Big Sur,
Em                F
   Hangin' a - round,
Em                          F
   Lettin' your old man down,
C               F            Dm
   Just don't go back to Big Sur,
G                              F/C
Baby, baby, please don't go.
     G                              C
Oh, baby, baby, please don't go.
```

Instrumental

Dmadd9	Cmaj7	Dmadd9	Cmaj7 Em	
F	Am	Dadd9	Dadd9
F	F G	Am	Am	

Chorus 3 As Chorus 2

The Boys Are Back In Town

Words & Music by Phil Lynott

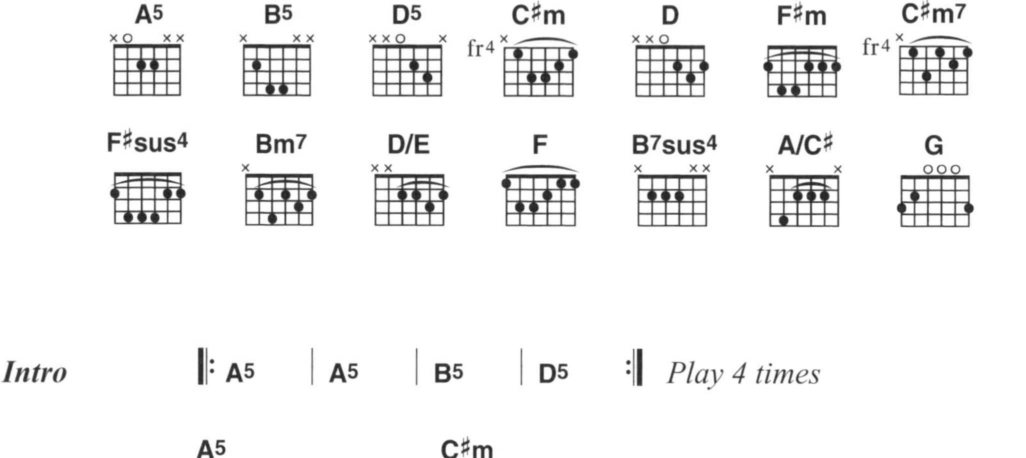

Intro ‖: A5 | A5 | B5 | D5 :‖ *Play 4 times*

Verse 1

```
A5                         C♯m
Guess who just got back today,
D                                F♯m
   Them wild-eyed boys that had been away.
C♯m7                      F♯sus4
  Haven't changed,   hadn't much to say,
Bm7                                D/E
   But man, I still think them cats are crazy.
A5                                 C♯m
   They were asking if you were around,
D                                  F
   How you was, where you could be found.
C♯m7                                    F♯sus4
   Told them you may be livin' downtown,
Bm7                                  D/E
   Driving all the old men   crazy.
```

Chorus 1

```
     A5                                                  B5
The boys are back in town, (the boys are back in town,)
D5          A5                              B5                   D5
   I said the boys are back in town, (the boys are back in town,)
     A5
The boys are back in town, (the boys are back in town,)
B5                    D5
The boys are back in town, (the boys are back in town.)
```

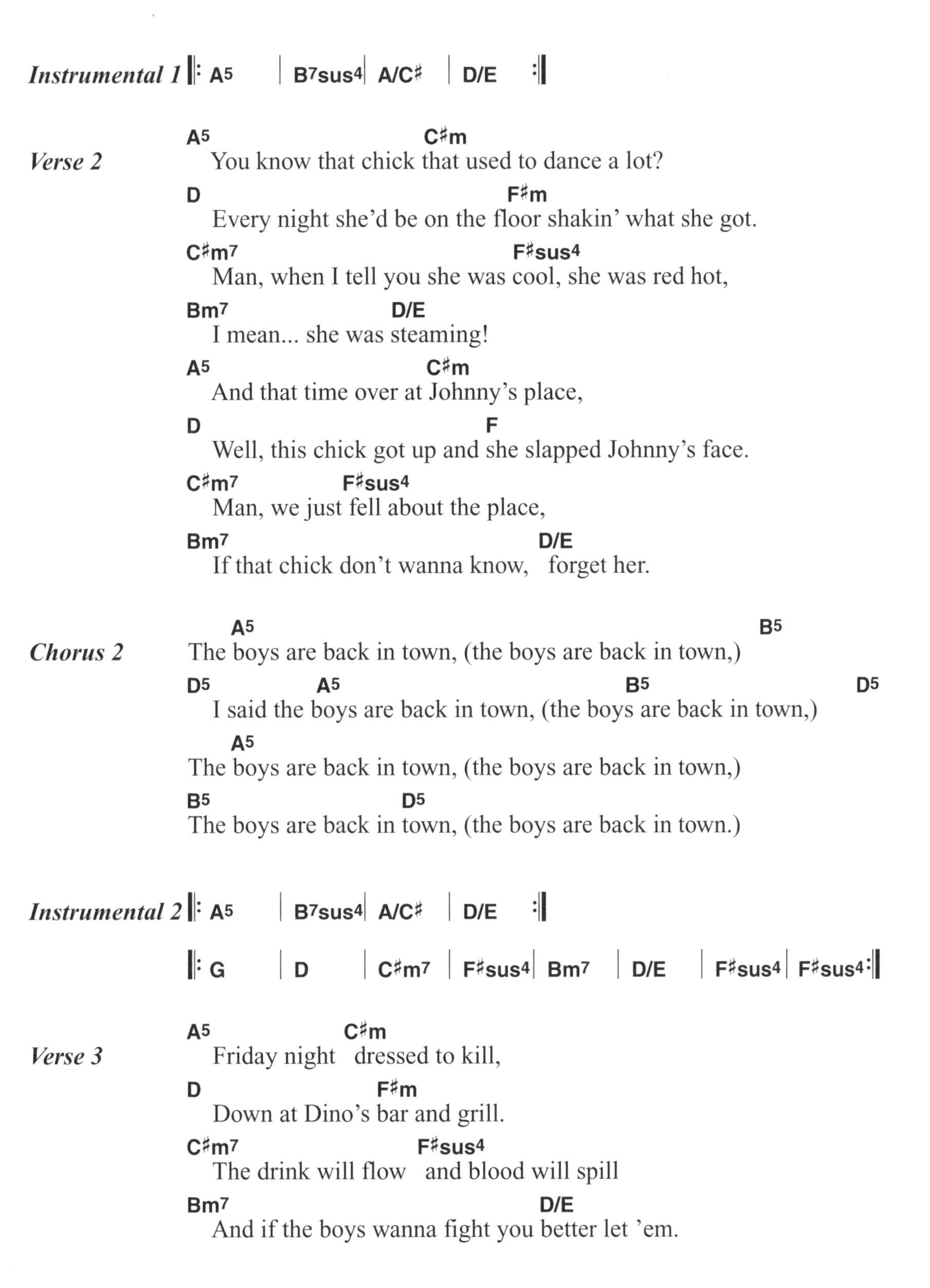

Instrumental 1 ‖: A5 | B7sus4 | A/C♯ | D/E :‖

Verse 2

A5 C♯m
You know that chick that used to dance a lot?
D F♯m
Every night she'd be on the floor shakin' what she got.
C♯m7 F♯sus4
Man, when I tell you she was cool, she was red hot,
Bm7 D/E
I mean... she was steaming!
A5 C♯m
And that time over at Johnny's place,
D F
Well, this chick got up and she slapped Johnny's face.
C♯m7 F♯sus4
Man, we just fell about the place,
Bm7 D/E
If that chick don't wanna know, forget her.

Chorus 2

A5 B5
The boys are back in town, (the boys are back in town,)
D5 A5 B5 D5
I said the boys are back in town, (the boys are back in town,)
A5
The boys are back in town, (the boys are back in town,)
B5 D5
The boys are back in town, (the boys are back in town.)

Instrumental 2 ‖: A5 | B7sus4 | A/C♯ | D/E :‖

‖: G | D | C♯m7 | F♯sus4 | Bm7 | D/E | F♯sus4 | F♯sus4 :‖

Verse 3

A5 C♯m
Friday night dressed to kill,
D F♯m
Down at Dino's bar and grill.
C♯m7 F♯sus4
The drink will flow and blood will spill
Bm7 D/E
And if the boys wanna fight you better let 'em.

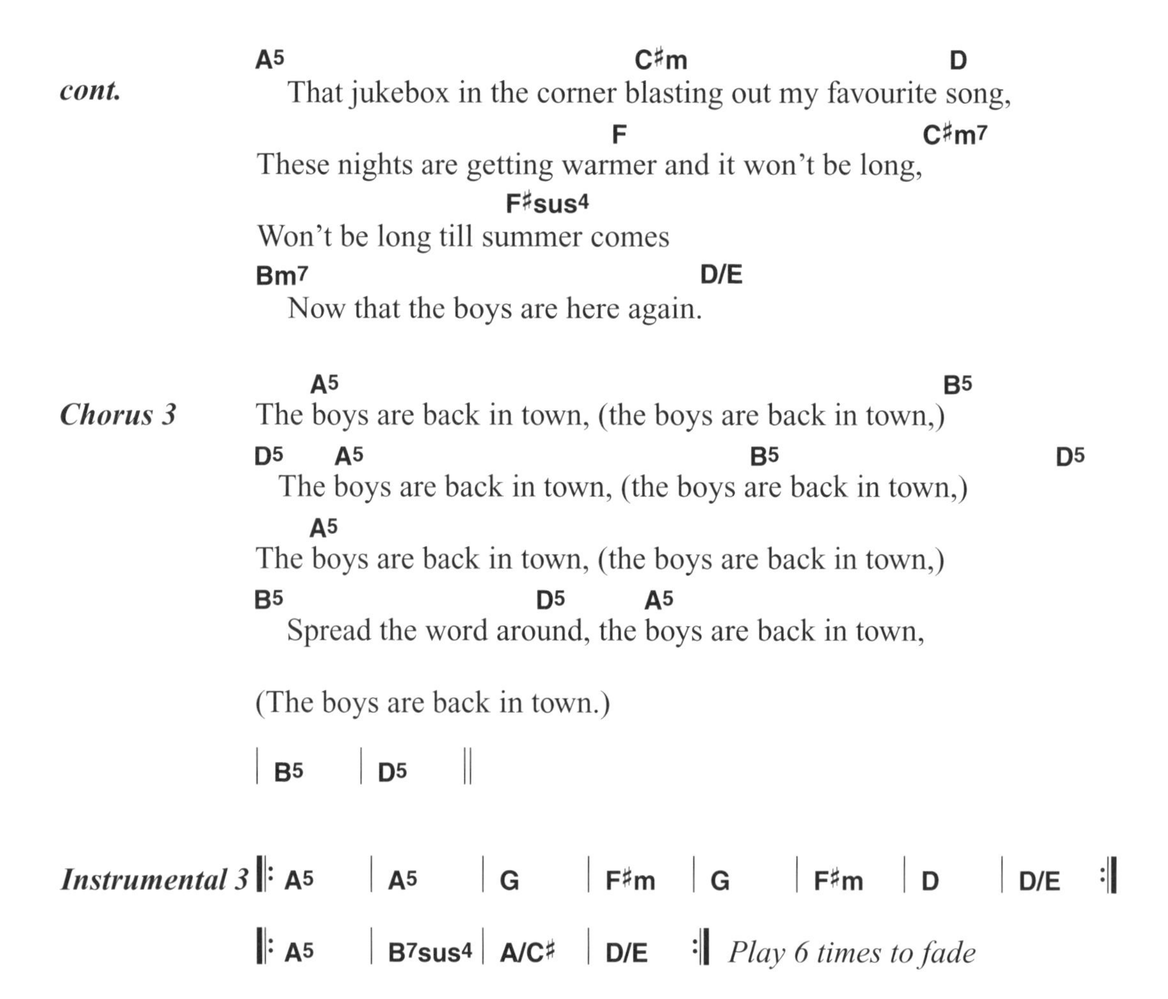

cont.

A5 C♯m D
That jukebox in the corner blasting out my favourite song,
F C♯m7
These nights are getting warmer and it won't be long,
F♯sus4
Won't be long till summer comes
Bm7 D/E
Now that the boys are here again.

Chorus 3

A5 B5
The boys are back in town, (the boys are back in town,)
D5 A5 B5 D5
The boys are back in town, (the boys are back in town,)
A5
The boys are back in town, (the boys are back in town,)
B5 D5 A5
Spread the word around, the boys are back in town,

(The boys are back in town.)

| B5 | D5 ||

Instrumental 3 |: A5 | A5 | G | F♯m | G | F♯m | D | D/E :|

|: A5 | B7sus4 | A/C♯ | D/E :| *Play 6 times to fade*

Brown Eyed Girl

Words & Music by Van Morrison

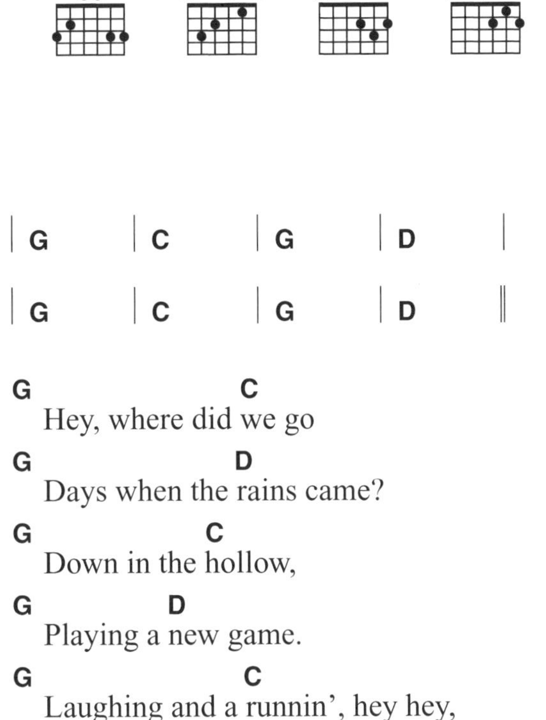

Intro

| G | C | G | D |

| G | C | G | D ||

Verse 1

G C
Hey, where did we go

G D
Days when the rains came?

G C
Down in the hollow,

G D
Playing a new game.

G C
Laughing and a runnin', hey hey,

G D
Skipping and a - jumpin'

G C
In the misty morning fog with

G D
Our, our hearts a - thumpin' and

Chorus 1

C D7 G Em
You, my brown eyed girl.

C D7 G D
And you, my brown eyed girl.

Verse 2

```
G                     C
   And what ever happened
G                      D
   To Tuesday and so slow?
G                           C
   Going down to the old mine
        G              D
With a   transistor radio.
G                       C
   Standing in the sunlight laughing,
G                         D
   Hiding behind a rainbow's wall.
G                       C
   Slipping and a - sliding
G                   D
   All along the waterfall with
```

Chorus 2

```
C     D7                        G     Em
You,     my brown eyed girl.
C              D7                  G     D7
   You, my      brown eyed girl.

Do you remember when
                 G
We used to sing
              C
Sha la la la la la la,
G                  D7
La la la la de da.

Just like that
G               C
   Sha la la la la la la,
G                  D7
La la la la de da,
       (G)
La de da.
```

Link

| G | G | G | G | G | C | G | D ||

Verse 3

G C
So hard to find my way
G D
Now that I'm all on my own
G C
I saw you just the other day
G D
My how you have grown
G C
Cast my memory back there, Lord
G D
Sometimes I'm overcome thinkin' about it
G C
Makin' love in the green grass
G D
Behind the stadium with

Chorus 3

C D7 G Em
You, my brown eyed girl
C D7 G D7
And you, my brown eyed girl.

Do you remember when
G
We used to sing
G C
𝄆 Sha la la la la la la,
G D7
La la la la de da.
(Lying in the green grass)
G C
Sha la la la la la la,
G D7
La la la la de da, 𝄇 *Repeat ad lib. to fade*

Carrickfergus

Traditional
Arranged by Brian Kennedy

⑥ = D ③ = F♯
⑤ = A ② = A
④ = D ① = D

Verse 1

```
               Em11  A7sus4          D       Bm7
I wish I was          in Carrick - fergus,
               Em11  A7sus4          D     A7sus4  D
Only for nights        in Bally - gran.
                   Em11  A7sus4           D       Bm7
I would swim over          the deepest ocean,
                 Em11  A7sus4               D      A7sus4  D
The deepest ocean         for my love to find.
                   Bm7                     A7sus4
But the sea is wide     and I cannot swim over,
              Bm7          A7sus4
Nor have I the wings to fly.
                       Em11  A7sus4           D            Bm7
But I wish I could find           a handsome    boatman
                 Em11  A7sus4                D     A7sus4  D
To ferry me over          to my love and die.
```

Verse 2

```
D                Em11  A7sus4                  D           Bm7
My childhood days          bring back sad re - flections
              Em11  A7sus4                  D    A7sus4  D
Of happy times          I spent so long a - go.
                 Em11  A7sus4               D        Bm7
My boyhood friends         and my own re - lations
                     Em11  A7sus4              D      A7sus4  D
Have all passed on now        like melting snow.
                     Bm7                  A7sus4
But I'll spend my       days in endless roaming,
              Bm7             A7sus4
Soft is the grass, my bed is free.
             Em11     A7sus4           D       Bm7
Ah, to be back now,        in Carrick - fergus,
                 Em11  A7sus4            D      A7sus4  D
On that long road         down to the sea.
```

Instr. | D | Bm7 | A7sus4 | A7sus4 |

| Bm7 | Bm7 | A7sus4 | A7sus4 ||

Verse 3

```
A7sus4          Em11  A7sus4          D          Bm7
And in Kil - kenny         it is re - ported
               Em11             A7sus4             D      A7sus4   D
There are marble stones          as black as ink.
                    Em11  A7sus4                  D          Bm7
With gold and silver           I would sup - port her,
                     Em11    A7sus4               D        A7sus4   D
But I'll sing no more  now      till I get a drink.
                             Bm7                     A7sus4
Sure I'm drunk today       and I'm seldom sober,
                Bm7                       A7sus4
A handsome rover from town to town.
                Em11       A7sus4                 D                Bm7
Ah, but I'm sick now        and my days are numbered,
                     Em11          A7sus4            D        A7sus4   D
So come all ye young men         and lay me down.
                     Em11          A7sus4            D        A7sus4   D
So come all ye young men         and lay me down.
```

Crazy World

Words & Music by Christy Dignam, Joe Jewell, Tony McGuinness,
Billy McGuinness & Alan Downey

D Em G Em7 A C

Intro | D | D | Em | Em |
| G | G | D | D ||

Chorus 1

```
D                                 Em
How can I protect you in this cra - zy world?
      G
It's all right, yeah,
      D
It's all right.
```

Verse 1

```
D                          Em
I have fallen down so many times,
Em7
Don't know why, don't know where,
                             D
Don't care less, it's all the same.
                                 Em
I have travelled through so many towns,
Em7
Don't know why, don't know where,
                             D
Don't care less, it's all the same.
```

Chorus 2 As Chorus 1

Verse 2

```
D                          Em
Can you hear the sound of nothing, nothing?
Em7
Nothing's right, nothing's wrong,
                             D
Don't care less, it's all the same.
```

cont.

```
Love is blind, love is real,
                                         Em
Don't you know that love is what you feel?
     Em7
It's all right, yeah,
     D
It's all right.
```

Chorus 3 As Chorus 1

Bridge 1

```
G                       D
  And when the talking's o - ver,
G                 D
  All the crowd has gone.

Nothing left I can do,
A                  G
Am I ever gonna get through to you?
     C     D
It's all right.
```

Instr.

```
| D     | D     | Em    | Em    |
| G     | G     | D     | D     |
| D     | D     | Em    | Em    ||
     G
It's all right,
                D
This is a crazy world.
```

Chorus 4 As Chorus 1

Bridge 2

```
D
How can I protect when all the crowd have gone?
Em
Now your party's over, all this world is wrong.
     G
It's all right, ooh,
     D
It's all right.
```

Chorus 5 As Chorus 1 *To fade*

Fairytale Of New York

Words & Music by Shane MacGowan & Jem Finer

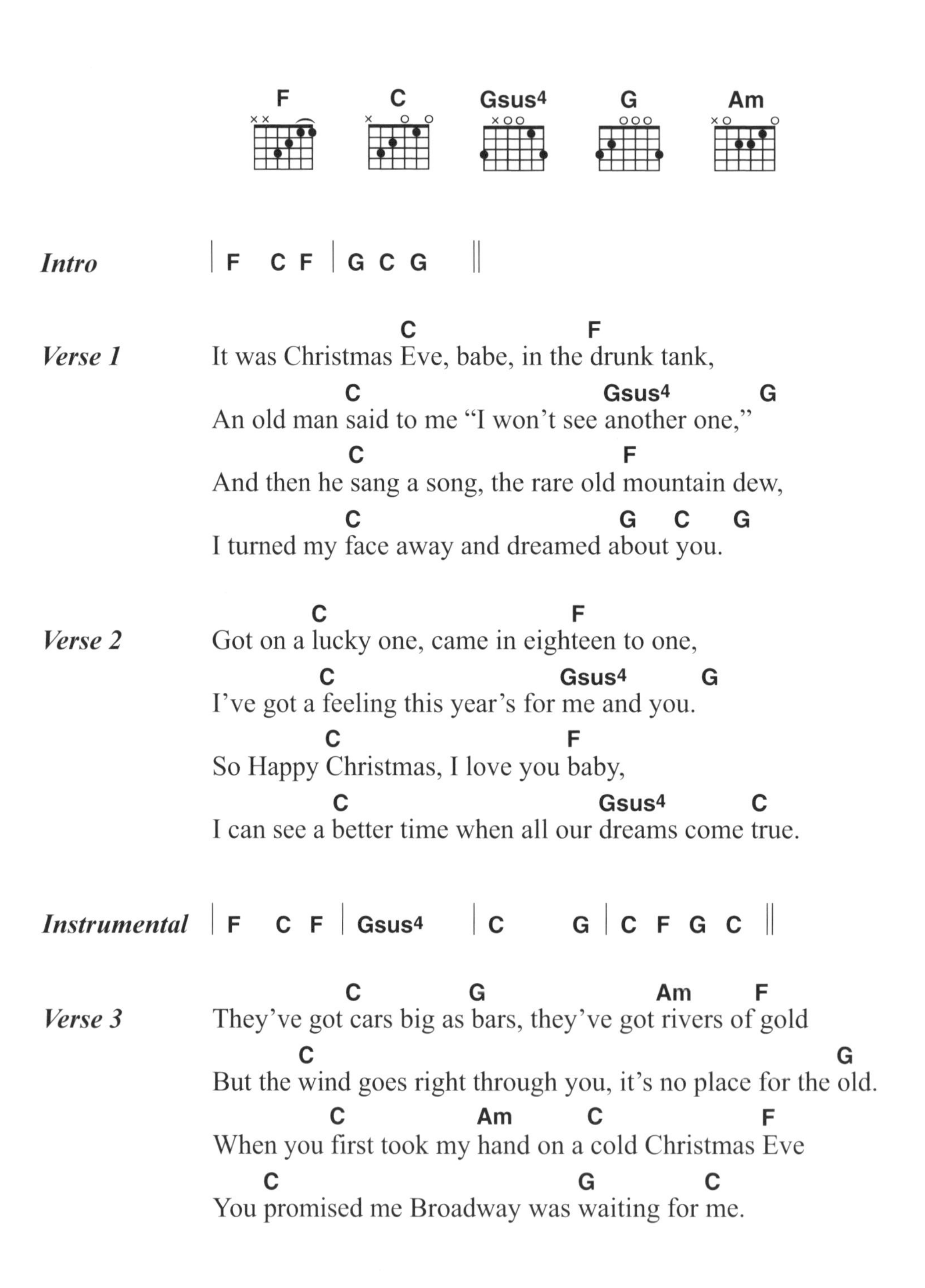

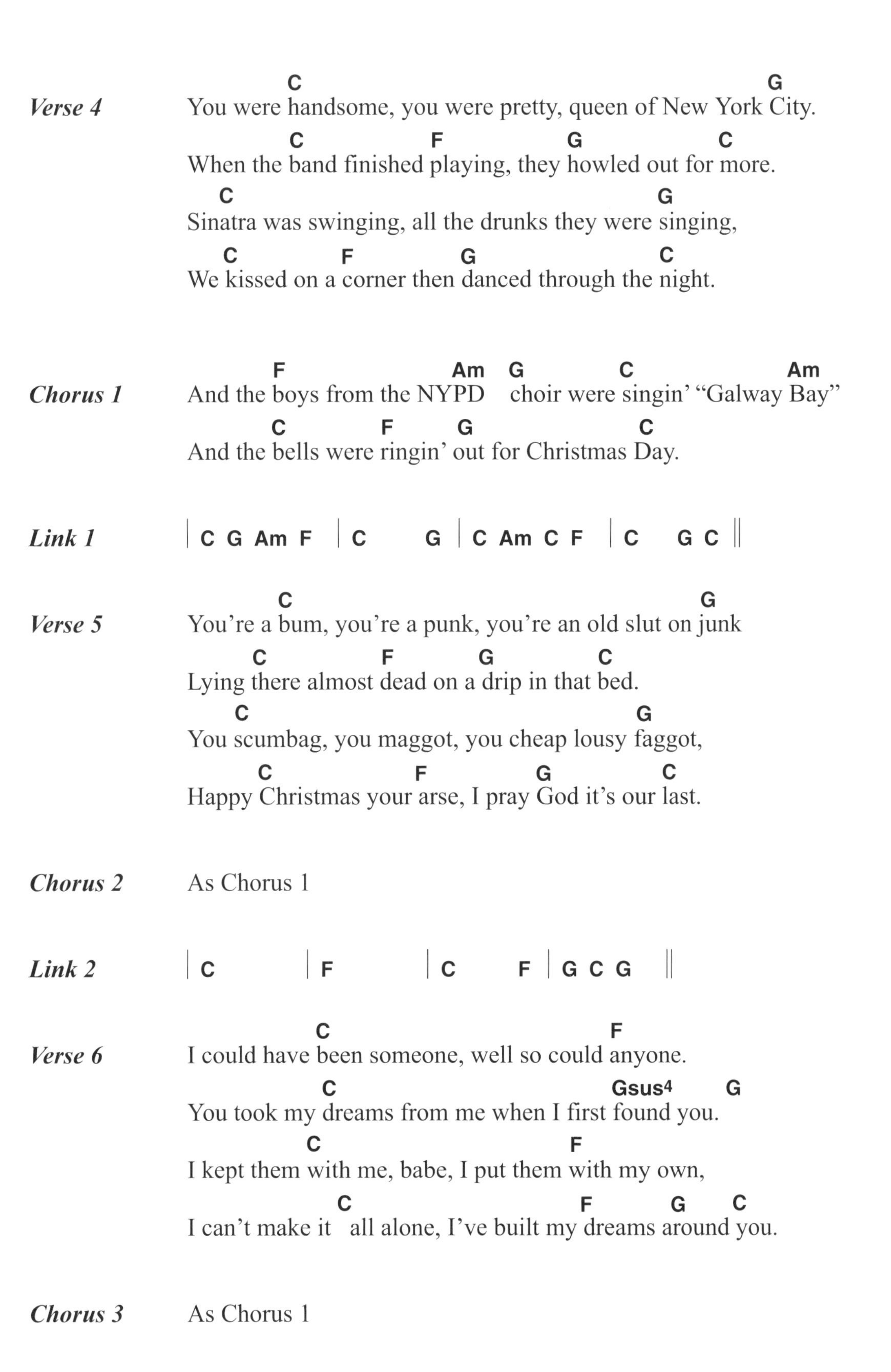

Verse 4

```
         C                                             G
You were handsome, you were pretty, queen of New York City.
         C             F        G                   C
When the band finished playing, they howled out for more.
    C                                          G
Sinatra was swinging, all the drunks they were singing,
   C           F           G                  C
We kissed on a corner then danced through the night.
```

Chorus 1

```
        F                  Am   G          C               Am
And the boys from the NYPD   choir were singin' "Galway Bay"
        C          F       G                 C
And the bells were ringin' out for Christmas Day.
```

Link 1

```
| C G Am F | C    G | C Am C F | C   G C ||
```

Verse 5

```
         C                                         G
You're a bum, you're a punk, you're an old slut on junk
      C            F         G            C
Lying there almost dead on a drip in that bed.
     C                                   G
You scumbag, you maggot, you cheap lousy faggot,
      C              F            G           C
Happy Christmas your arse, I pray God it's our last.
```

Chorus 2

As Chorus 1

Link 2

```
| C      | F      | C     F | G C G  ||
```

Verse 6

```
             C                           F
I could have been someone, well so could anyone.
            C                           Gsus4     G
You took my dreams from me when I first found you.
            C                         F
I kept them with me, babe, I put them with my own,
                  C                        F      G      C
I can't make it   all alone, I've built my dreams around you.
```

Chorus 3

As Chorus 1

Fisherman's Blues

Words & Music by Mike Scott & Steve Wickham

G F Am C

Intro |: G | G | F | F | Am | Am | C | C :|

Verse 1
```
G                         F
I wish I was a fisherman tumbling on the seas,
Am                                C
   Far away from dry land and its bitter memories,
G                                    F
   Casting out my sweet life with abandonment and love,
Am                                              C
   No ceiling bearing down on me save the starry sky above.
                    G
With light in my head,
                     F   G  Am  | Am  ||
And you in my arms.    Whoo!
```

Link 1 | G | G | F | F | Am | Am | C | C ||

Verse 2
```
G                              F
I wish I was the brakeman on a hurtling fevered train,
              Am                                 C
Crashing a-headlong into the heartland like a cannon in the rain,
          G                                F
With the beating of the sleepers and the burning of the coal,
Am                                   C
Counting the towns flashing by and the night that's full of soul.
                    G
With light in my head,
                     F   G  Am  | Am  ||
And you in my arms.    Whoo!
```

Link 2 |: G | G | F | F | Am | Am | C | C :|

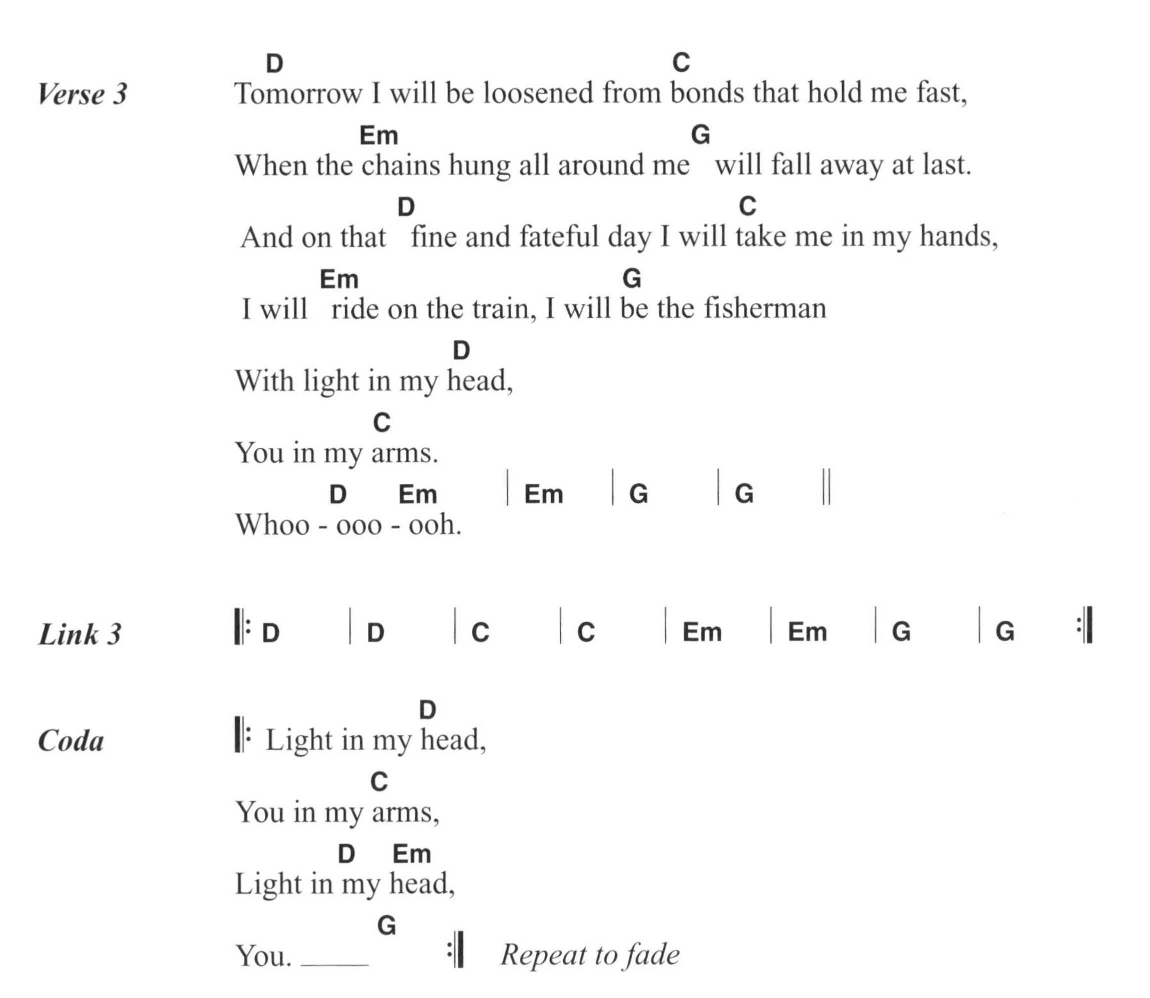

Verse 3

D — C
Tomorrow I will be loosened from bonds that hold me fast,
Em — G
When the chains hung all around me will fall away at last.
D — C
And on that fine and fateful day I will take me in my hands,
Em — G
I will ride on the train, I will be the fisherman
D
With light in my head,
C
You in my arms.
D Em | Em | G | G ||
Whoo - ooo - ooh.

Link 3

|: D | D | C | C | Em | Em | G | G :|

Coda

D
|: Light in my head,
C
You in my arms,
D Em
Light in my head,
G
You. ____ :| *Repeat to fade*

Freewheel

Words & Music by Peter Wilson

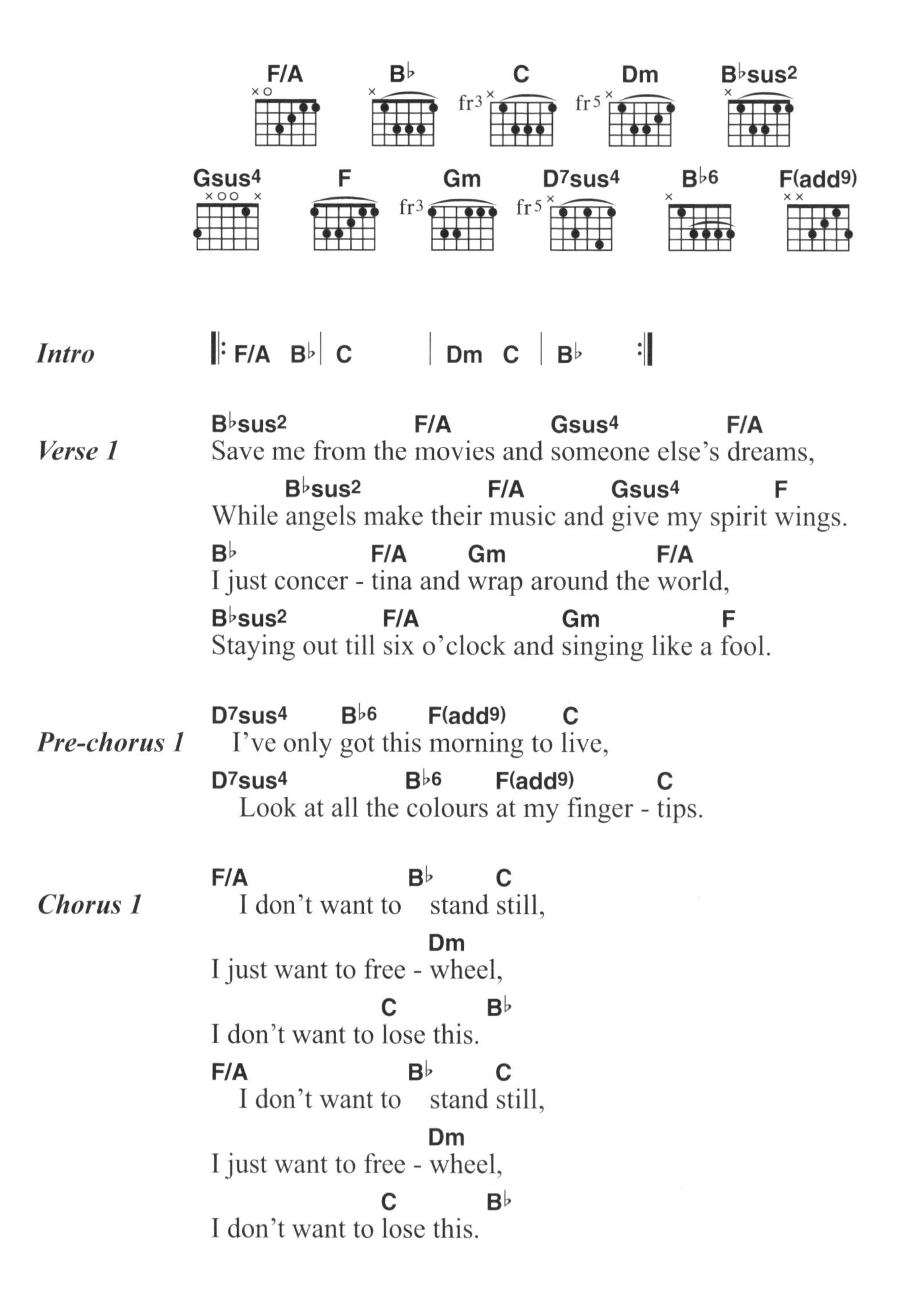

Verse 2

```
Bb                    F/A                 Gm         F/A
Save my feet from dancing with just anyone at all,
Bb                         F/A                 Gm              F
Worn out shoes 'cause lotus blue keeps hanging in the hall.
             Bb           F/A          Gm                F/A
You're this face in the distance I hope to recog - nise,
             Bb                       F/A
But it's like running through deep water
          Gm              F
Trying to look into your eyes.
```

Pre-chorus 2 As Pre-chorus 1

Chorus 2 As Chorus 1

Bridge 1

```
Bb
Come on, come on, come on.

Come on, come on, come on.

Come on, come on, come on, come on,

Come on, come on, come on, come on,
                         F/A   Bb  C  Dm  C  Bb
Come on, come on, my soul.________________
```

Chorus 3 As Chorus 1

Girl From Mars

Words & Music by Tim Wheeler

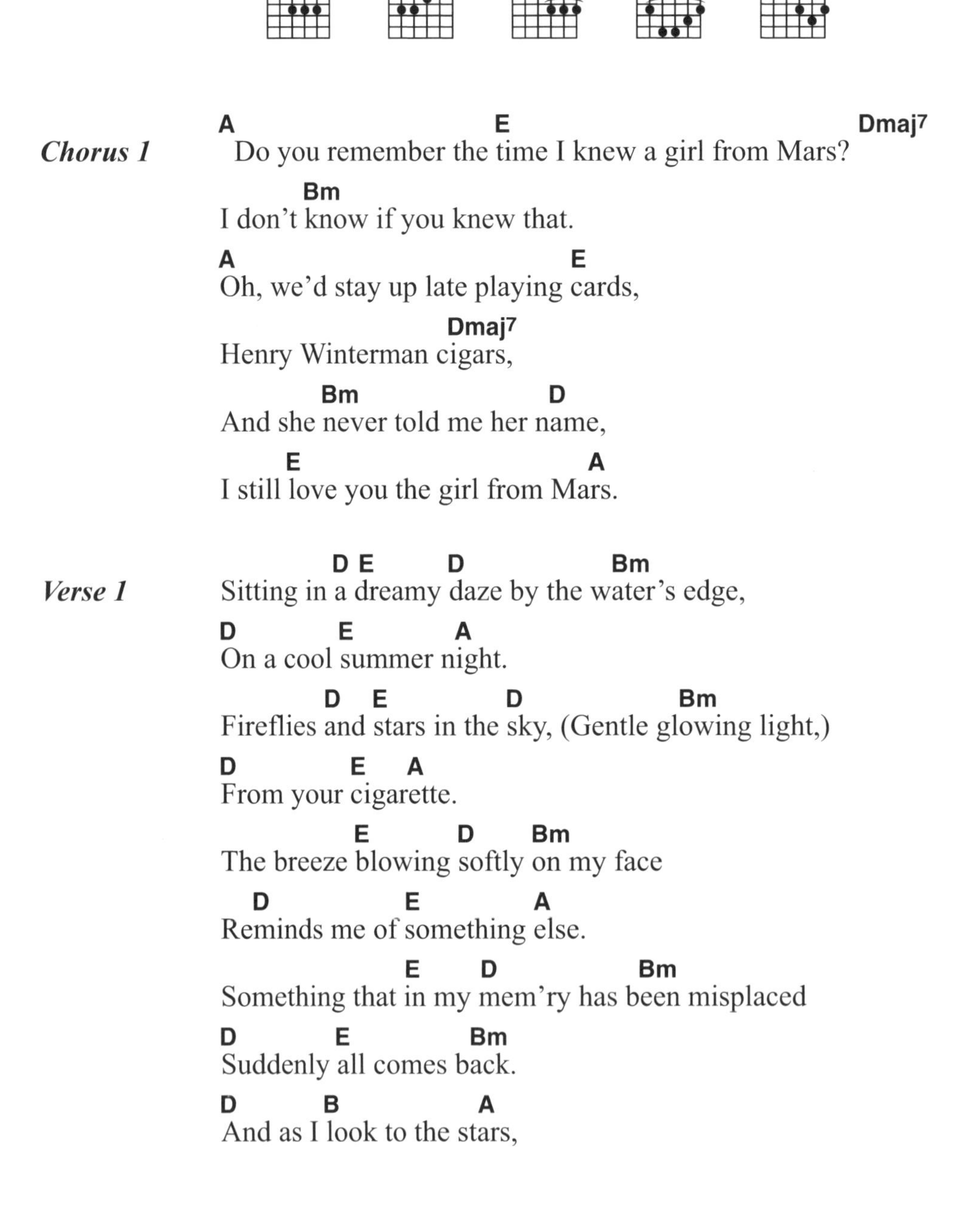

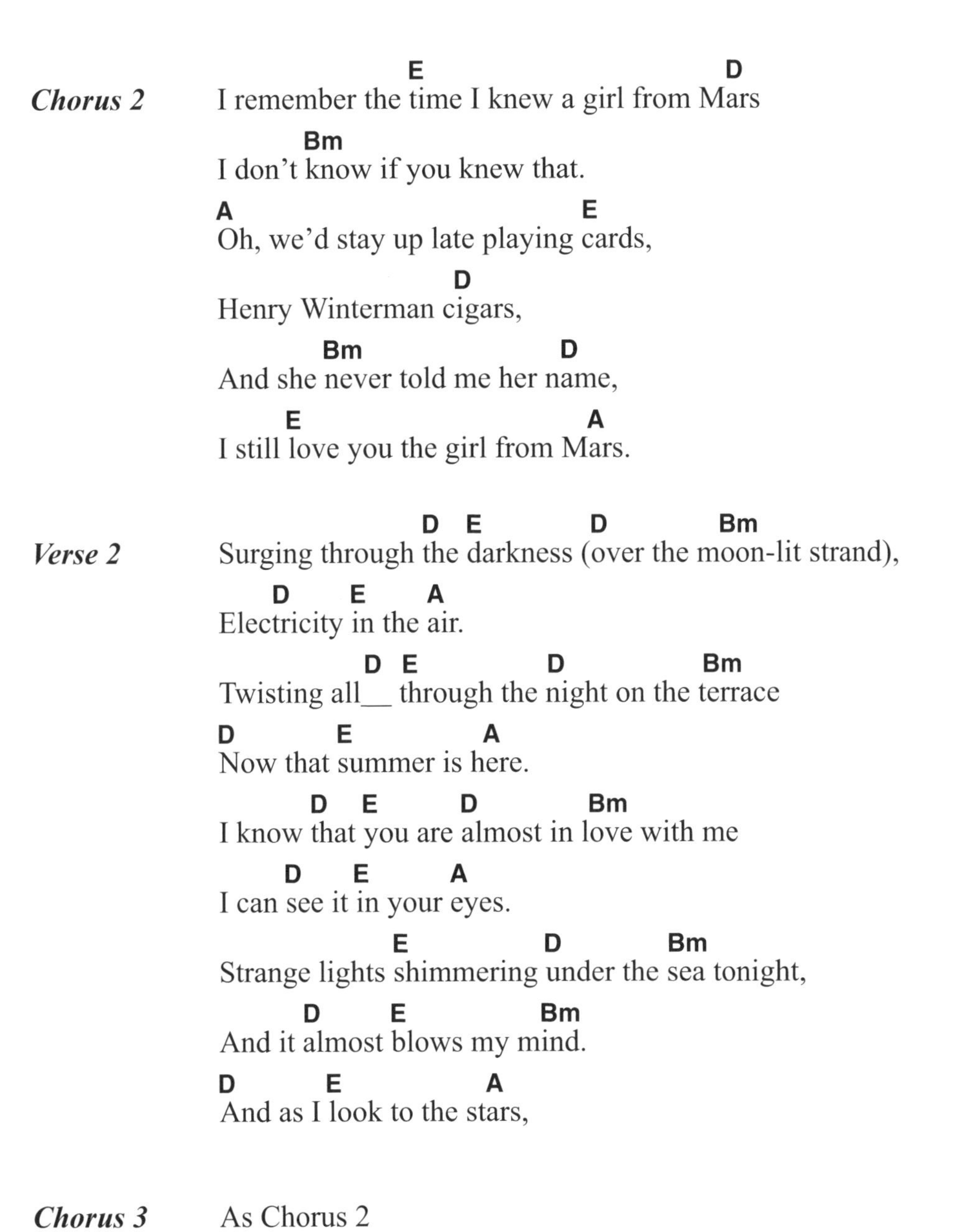

```
                          E                       D
Chorus 2    I remember the time I knew a girl from Mars

                Bm
            I don't know if you knew that.

            A                          E
            Oh, we'd stay up late playing cards,

                                 D
            Henry Winterman cigars,

                    Bm                   D
            And she never told me her name,

                  E                      A
            I still love you the girl from Mars.


                                D  E         D          Bm
Verse 2     Surging through the darkness (over the moon-lit strand),

               D    E     A
            Electricity in the air.

                           D E          D           Bm
            Twisting all__ through the night on the terrace

            D         E        A
            Now that summer is here.

                    D  E      D         Bm
            I know that you are almost in love with me

                  D    E     A
            I can see it in your eyes.

                              E         D        Bm
            Strange lights shimmering under the sea tonight,

                    D    E        Bm
            And it almost blows my mind.

            D        E          A
            And as I look to the stars,


Chorus 3    As Chorus 2
```

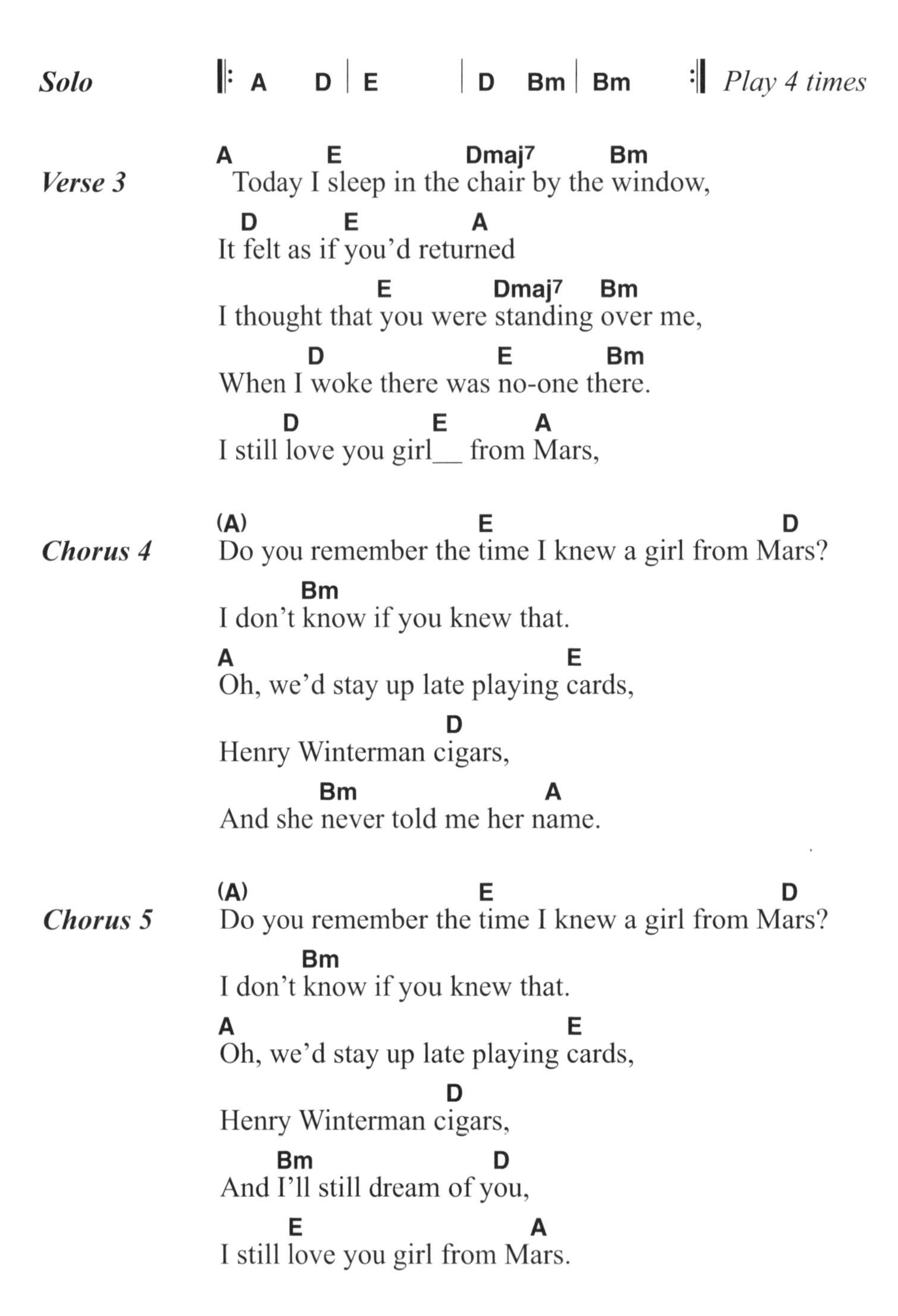

Solo 𝄆 A D | E | D Bm | Bm 𝄇 *Play 4 times*

Verse 3

A E Dmaj7 Bm
Today I sleep in the chair by the window,
D E A
It felt as if you'd returned
E Dmaj7 Bm
I thought that you were standing over me,
D E Bm
When I woke there was no-one there.
D E A
I still love you girl__ from Mars,

Chorus 4

(A) E D
Do you remember the time I knew a girl from Mars?
Bm
I don't know if you knew that.
A E
Oh, we'd stay up late playing cards,
D
Henry Winterman cigars,
Bm A
And she never told me her name.

Chorus 5

(A) E D
Do you remember the time I knew a girl from Mars?
Bm
I don't know if you knew that.
A E
Oh, we'd stay up late playing cards,
D
Henry Winterman cigars,
Bm D
And I'll still dream of you,
E A
I still love you girl from Mars.

A Good Heart

Words & Music by Maria McKee

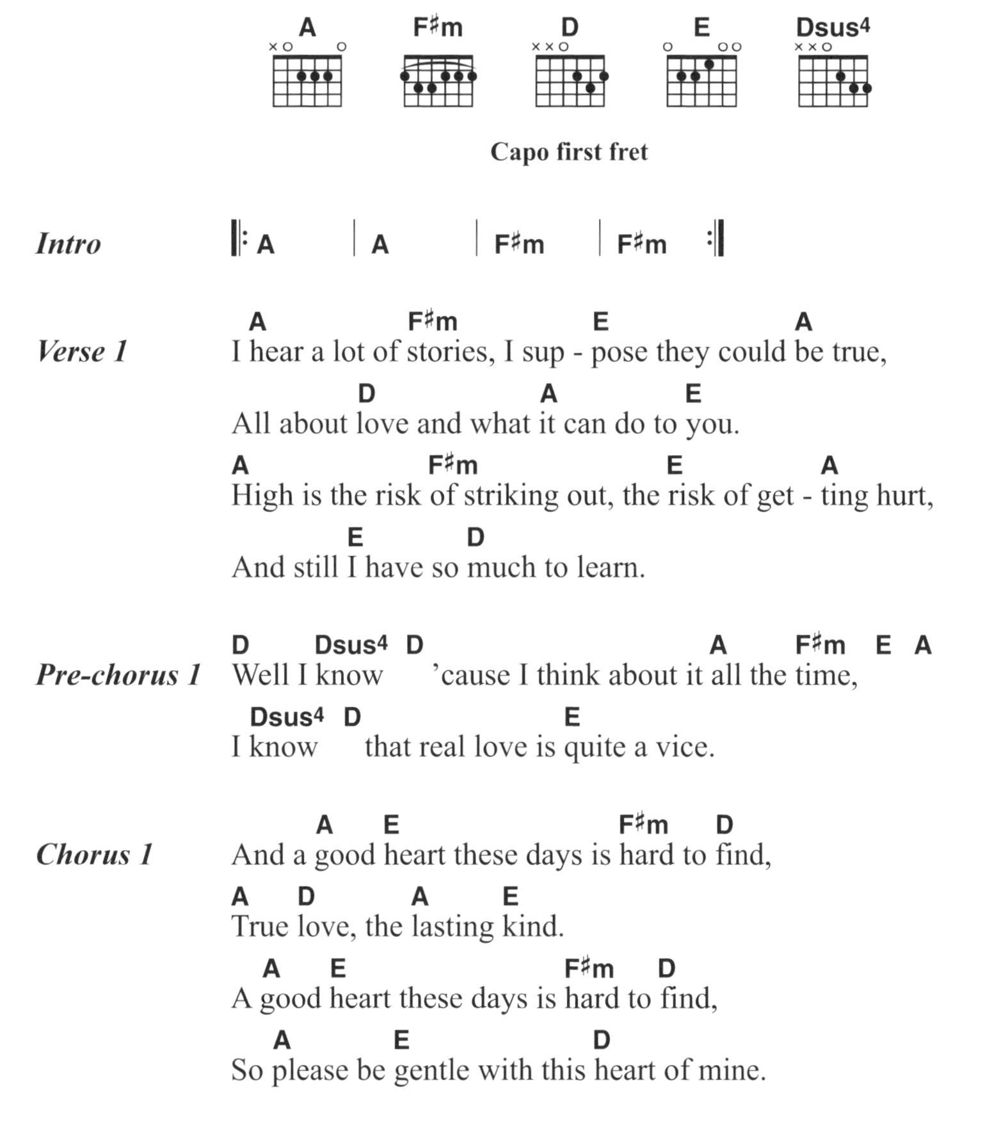

Capo first fret

Intro ‖: A | A | F♯m | F♯m :‖

Verse 1

A F♯m E A
I hear a lot of stories, I sup - pose they could be true,
D A E
All about love and what it can do to you.
A F♯m E A
High is the risk of striking out, the risk of get - ting hurt,
E D
And still I have so much to learn.

Pre-chorus 1

D Dsus4 D A F♯m E A
Well I know 'cause I think about it all the time,
Dsus4 D E
I know that real love is quite a vice.

Chorus 1

A E F♯m D
And a good heart these days is hard to find,
A D A E
True love, the lasting kind.
A E F♯m D
A good heart these days is hard to find,
A E D
So please be gentle with this heart of mine.

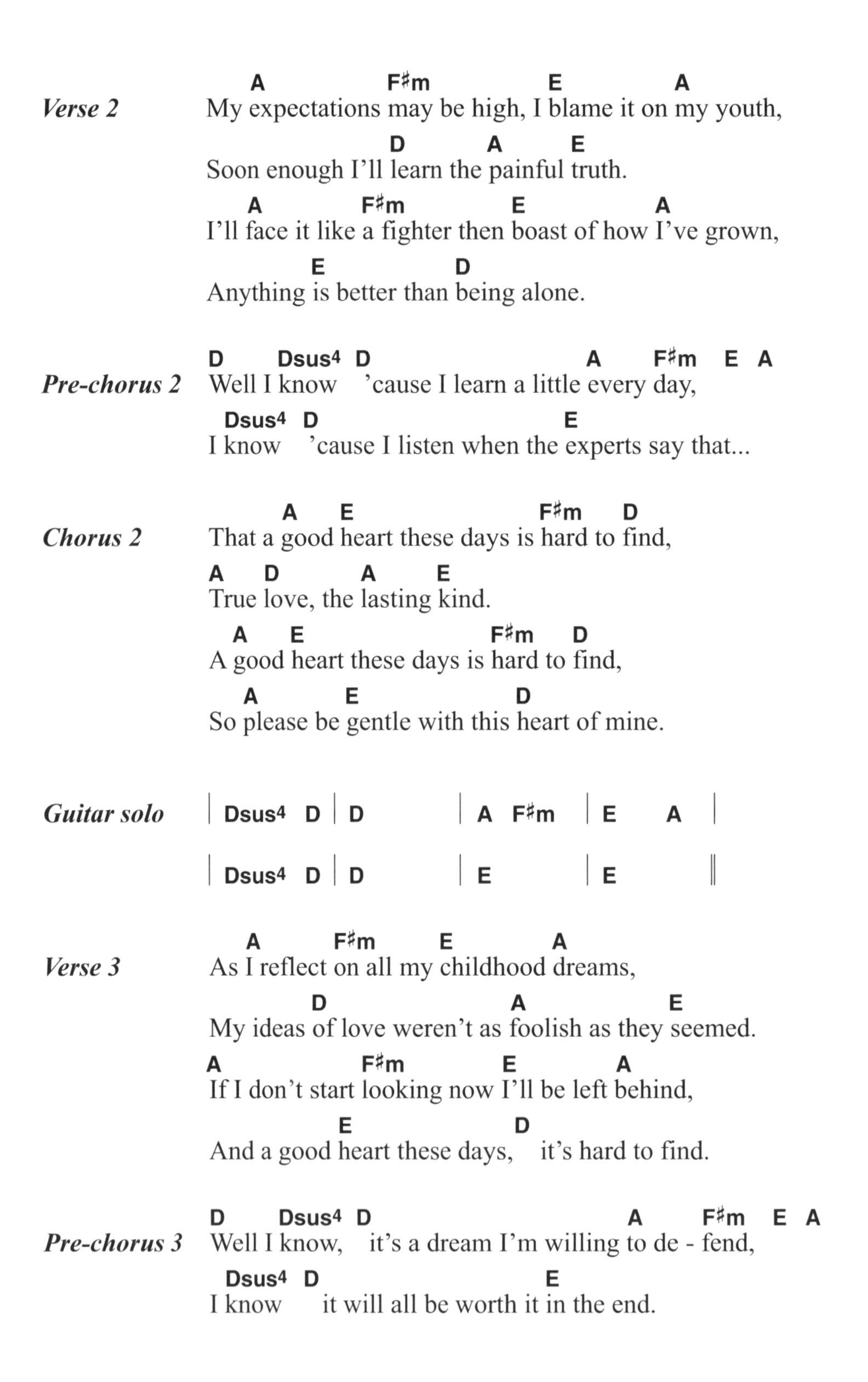

Verse 2

A F♯m E A
My expectations may be high, I blame it on my youth,

D A E
Soon enough I'll learn the painful truth.

A F♯m E A
I'll face it like a fighter then boast of how I've grown,

E D
Anything is better than being alone.

Pre-chorus 2

D Dsus4 D A F♯m E A
Well I know 'cause I learn a little every day,

Dsus4 D E
I know 'cause I listen when the experts say that...

Chorus 2

A E F♯m D
That a good heart these days is hard to find,

A D A E
True love, the lasting kind.

A E F♯m D
A good heart these days is hard to find,

A E D
So please be gentle with this heart of mine.

Guitar solo

| Dsus4 D | D | A F♯m | E A |

| Dsus4 D | D | E | E ||

Verse 3

A F♯m E A
As I reflect on all my childhood dreams,

D A E
My ideas of love weren't as foolish as they seemed.

A F♯m E A
If I don't start looking now I'll be left behind,

E D
And a good heart these days, it's hard to find.

Pre-chorus 3

D Dsus4 D A F♯m E A
Well I know, it's a dream I'm willing to de - fend,

Dsus4 D E
I know it will all be worth it in the end.

Chorus 3 As Chorus 1

Chorus 4

```
          A      E                                F♯m      D
And a good heart these days is hard to find,
A     D          A        E
True love, the lasting kind.
   A      E                            F♯m      D
A good heart these days is hard to find,
    A           E                       D        E                        A
So please be gentle with this heart, with this heart of mine.
```

Outro

```
Dsus4  D  Dsus4  D           A
                          A good heart.
            Dsus4  D  Dsus4  D
|: A good heart.
          A
A good heart. :|   Repeat to fade
```

Gloria

Words & Music by Van Morrison

E D A E* D* A* E**

fr12 fr10 fr9 fr4

Intro | E D A | E D A | E D A ||

Verse 1

E D A E D A
Wanna tell you about my baby:

E D A E D A
You know she comes around,

E D A E D A
She's about five feet four

E D A E D A
From her head to the ground.

E D A E D A
You know she comes around here

E D A E D A
A-just about midnight,

E D A E D A
She make me feel so good, Lord,

E D A E D A
She make me feel alright.

E D A E D A E D A
And her name is G. ______ L. ______

E D A E D A E D A
O. ______ R. ______ I. ______

Chorus 1

E D A E D A E
G. L. O. R. I. A, Glo - ri - a,

E D A E D A E
G. L. O. R. I. A, Glo - ri - a,

D A E D A E
I'm gonna shout it out now, Glo - ri - a,

D A E D A E
I'm gonna shout it everyday, Glo - ri - a,

D A
Yeah, yeah, yeah, yeah, yeah.

```
Link 1         | E   D A | E   D A ||

Guitar solo    ||: E*   D* A* D* | E*   D* A* D* :|| Play 3 times

Link 2         ||: E**  D A | E**  D A :|| E   D A ||

               E  D           A      E    D A
Verse 2             She comes around here
               E     D    A          E    D A
                  Just about midnight,
               E               D  A   E     D A
                  She make me feel   so good,
               E                 D           A  E    D A
                  I wanna say she makes me feel al - right.
               E              D        A         E    D A
                  'Cause she's walking down my street
               E                 D       A  E      D A
                  Why don't'cha come to my house,
               E               D  A          E   D A
                  She knock upon my door,
               E                D        A  E       D A
                  And then she come to my room,
               E                      D  A        E   D A
                  Then she make me feel alright.

               E           D A    E    D   A  E
Chorus 2          G. L. O. R. I. A, Glo  -  ri - a,
               E           D A    E    D   A  E
                  G. L. O. R. I. A, Glo  -  ri - a,
                           D        A        E    D    A  E
               I'm gonna shout it out now, Glo   -   ri - a,
                           D        A          E    D    A  E
               I'm gonna shout it everyday, Glo   -   ri - a,

               Yeah, yeah, yeah, yeah, yeah.

               D       A  E     D A        E
Coda              She's so  good,        well alright,
               D       A  E     D A        E    D A
                  She's so  good,        well alright.

               | E   D A | E   D A | E*   D* A* D* |

               | E*   D* A* D* | E*   D* A* D* | E      ||
```

The Great Song Of Indifference

Words & Music by Bob Geldof

Capo fourth fret

Intro | E | Asus2 | E | Bsus4 |
| E | Asus2 | E Bsus4 | E ||

Verse 1

```
E                 Asus2
I don't mind if you go,
E                         Bsus4
I don't mind if you take it slow,
E                              Asus2
I don't mind if you say yes or no,
E         Bsus4   E
I don't mind at all.
E                        Asus2
I don't care if you live or die,
E                               Bsus4
Couldn't care less if you laugh or cry,
E                         Asus2
I don't mind if you crash or fly,
E         Bsus4   E
I don't mind at all.
E                         Asus2
I don't mind if you come or go,
E                   Bsus4
I don't mind if you say no,
E                              Asus2
Couldn't care less baby let it flow,
          E       Bsus4  E
'Cause I don't care at all.
```

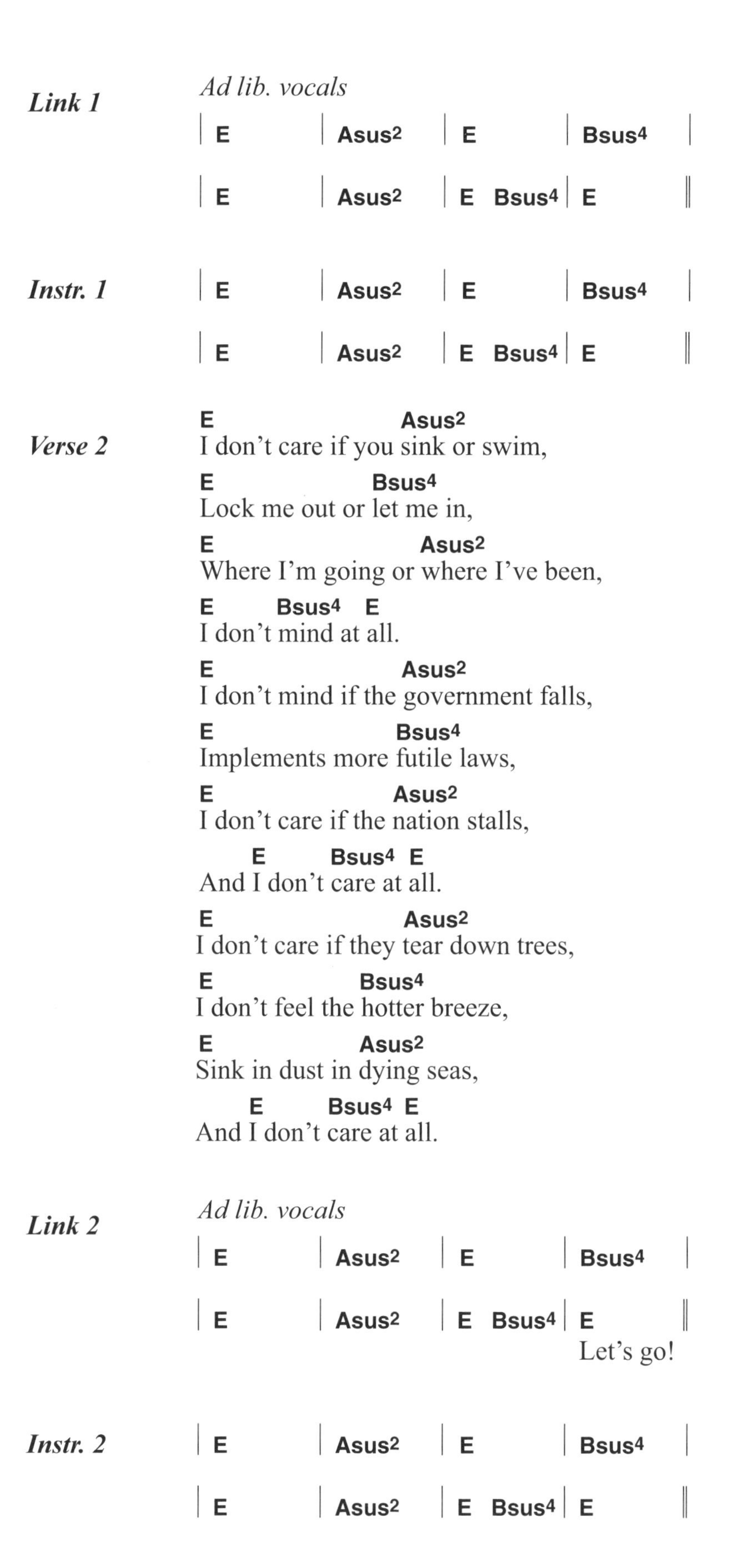

Link 1

Ad lib. vocals

| E | Asus2 | E | Bsus4 |

| E | Asus2 | E Bsus4 | E ||

Instr. 1

| E | Asus2 | E | Bsus4 |

| E | Asus2 | E Bsus4 | E ||

Verse 2

E Asus2
I don't care if you sink or swim,
E Bsus4
Lock me out or let me in,
E Asus2
Where I'm going or where I've been,
E Bsus4 E
I don't mind at all.
E Asus2
I don't mind if the government falls,
E Bsus4
Implements more futile laws,
E Asus2
I don't care if the nation stalls,
E Bsus4 E
And I don't care at all.
E Asus2
I don't care if they tear down trees,
E Bsus4
I don't feel the hotter breeze,
E Asus2
Sink in dust in dying seas,
E Bsus4 E
And I don't care at all.

Link 2

Ad lib. vocals

| E | Asus2 | E | Bsus4 |

| E | Asus2 | E Bsus4 | E ||
Let's go!

Instr. 2

| E | Asus2 | E | Bsus4 |

| E | Asus2 | E Bsus4 | E ||

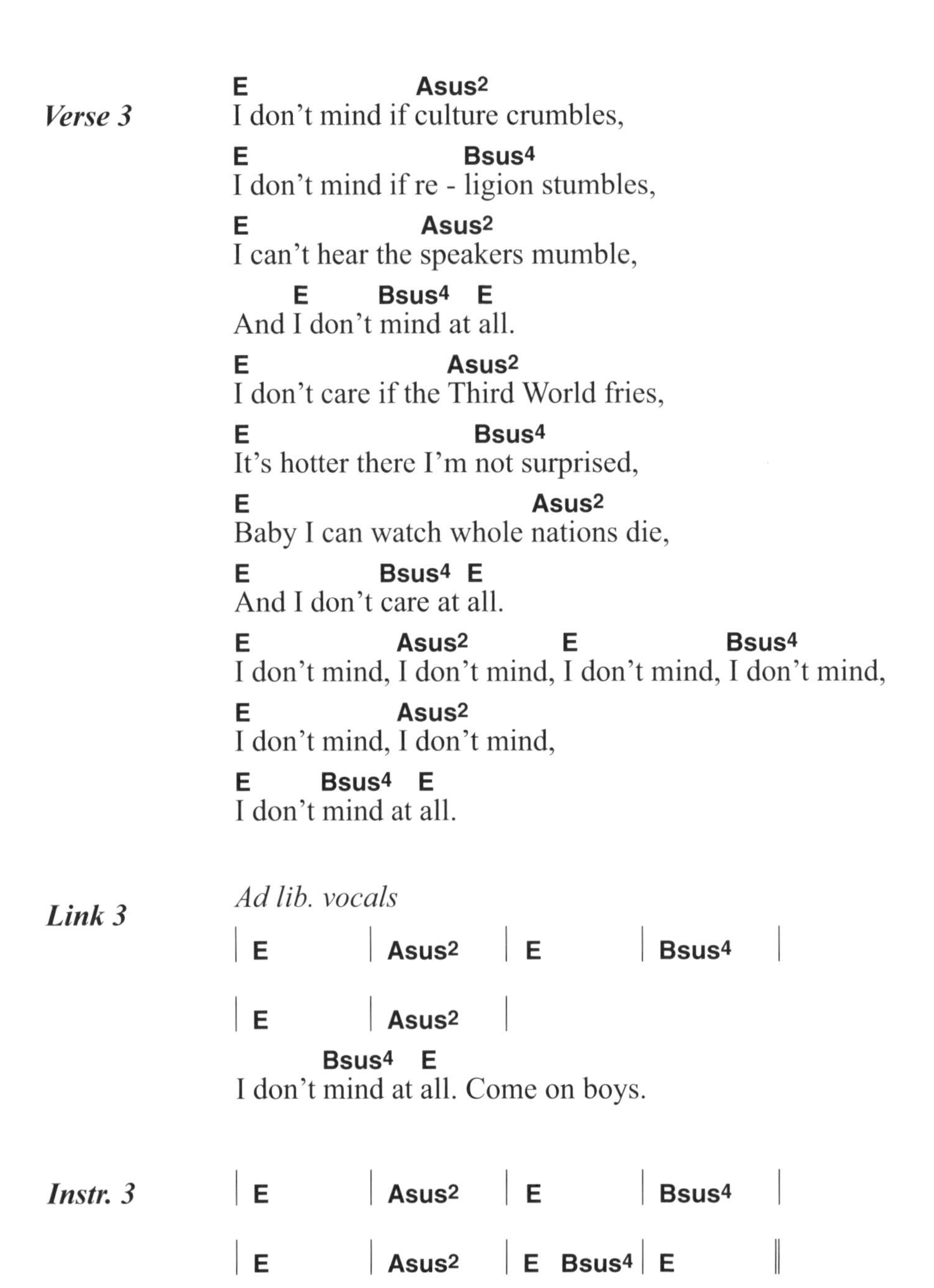

Verse 3

E Asus2
I don't mind if culture crumbles,
E Bsus4
I don't mind if re - ligion stumbles,
E Asus2
I can't hear the speakers mumble,
E Bsus4 E
And I don't mind at all.
E Asus2
I don't care if the Third World fries,
E Bsus4
It's hotter there I'm not surprised,
E Asus2
Baby I can watch whole nations die,
E Bsus4 E
And I don't care at all.
E Asus2 E Bsus4
I don't mind, I don't mind, I don't mind, I don't mind,
E Asus2
I don't mind, I don't mind,
E Bsus4 E
I don't mind at all.

Link 3

Ad lib. vocals

| E | Asus2 | E | Bsus4 |

| E | Asus2 |

Bsus4 E
I don't mind at all. Come on boys.

Instr. 3

| E | Asus2 | E | Bsus4 |

| E | Asus2 | E Bsus4 | E ||

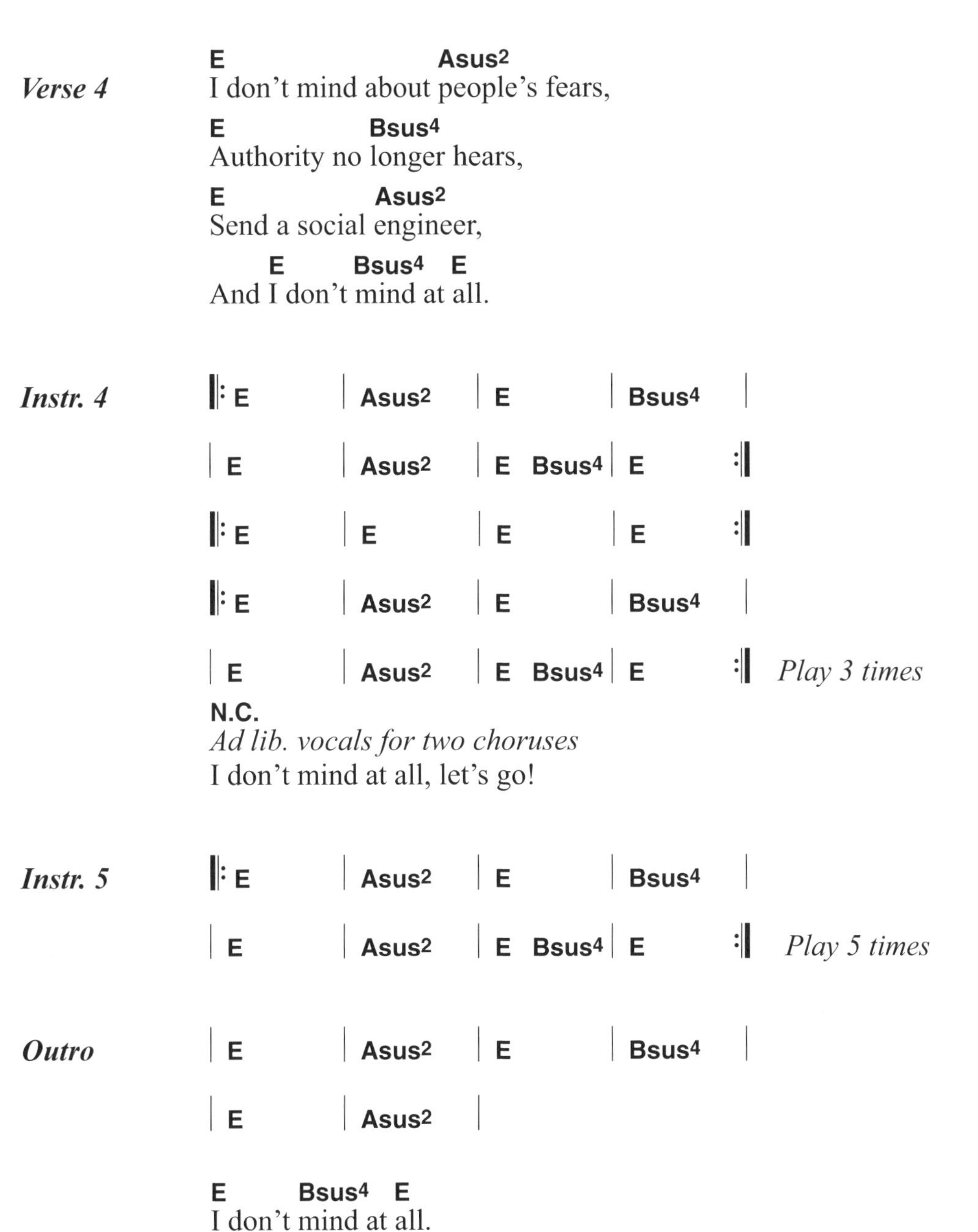
Verse 4
E Asus2
I don't mind about people's fears,
E Bsus4
Authority no longer hears,
E Asus2
Send a social engineer,
E Bsus4 E
And I don't mind at all.
Instr. 4
: E	Asus2	E	Bsus4
E	Asus2	E Bsus4	E :
: E	E	E	E :
: E	Asus2	E	Bsus4
E	Asus2	E Bsus4	E :| Play 3 times
N.C.
Ad lib. vocals for two choruses
I don't mind at all, let's go!
Instr. 5
: E	Asus2	E	Bsus4
E	Asus2	E Bsus4	E :| Play 5 times
Outro
E	Asus2	E	Bsus4
E	Asus2
E Bsus4 E
I don't mind at all.

I Don't Like Mondays

Words & Music by Bob Geldof

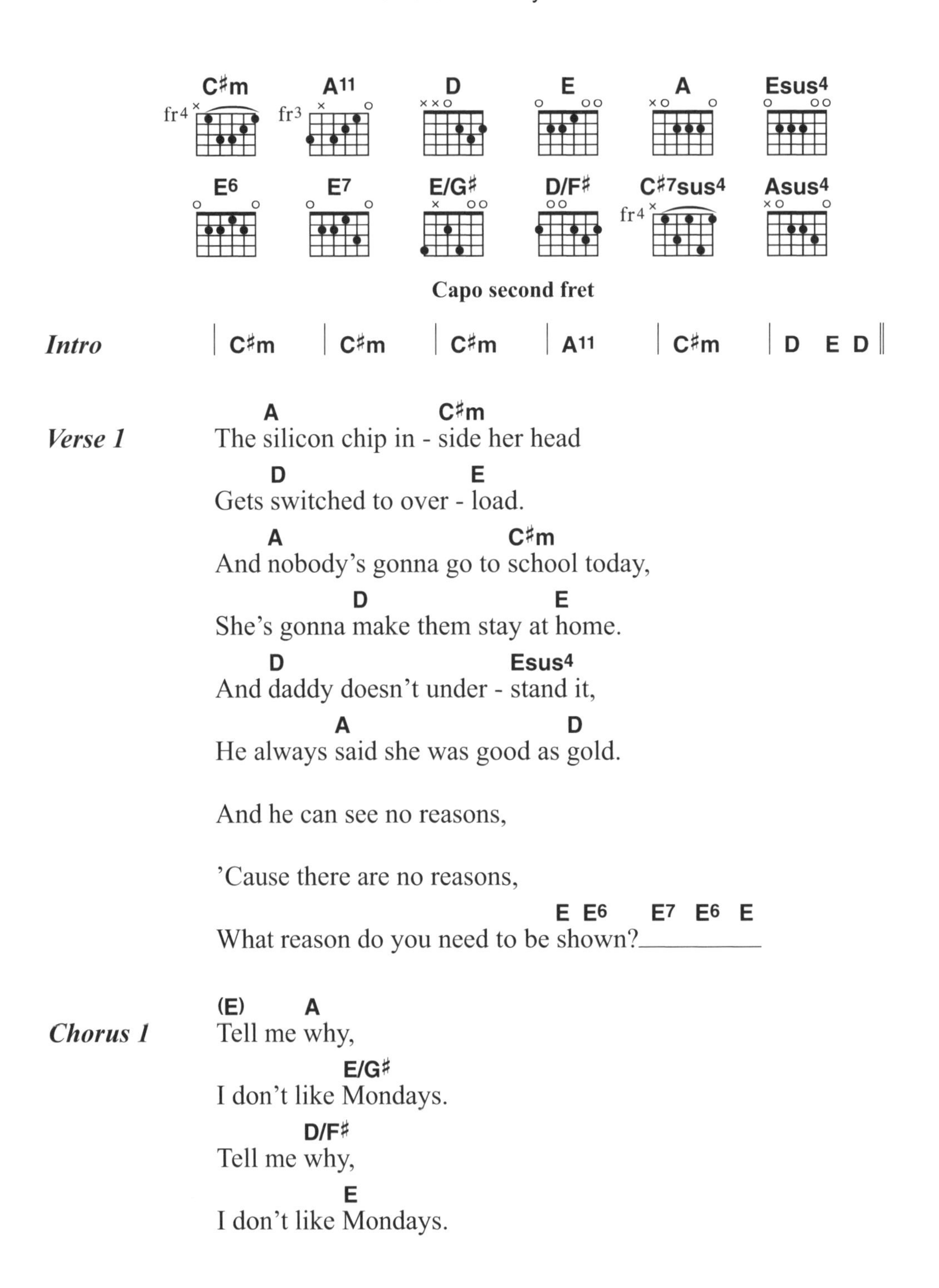

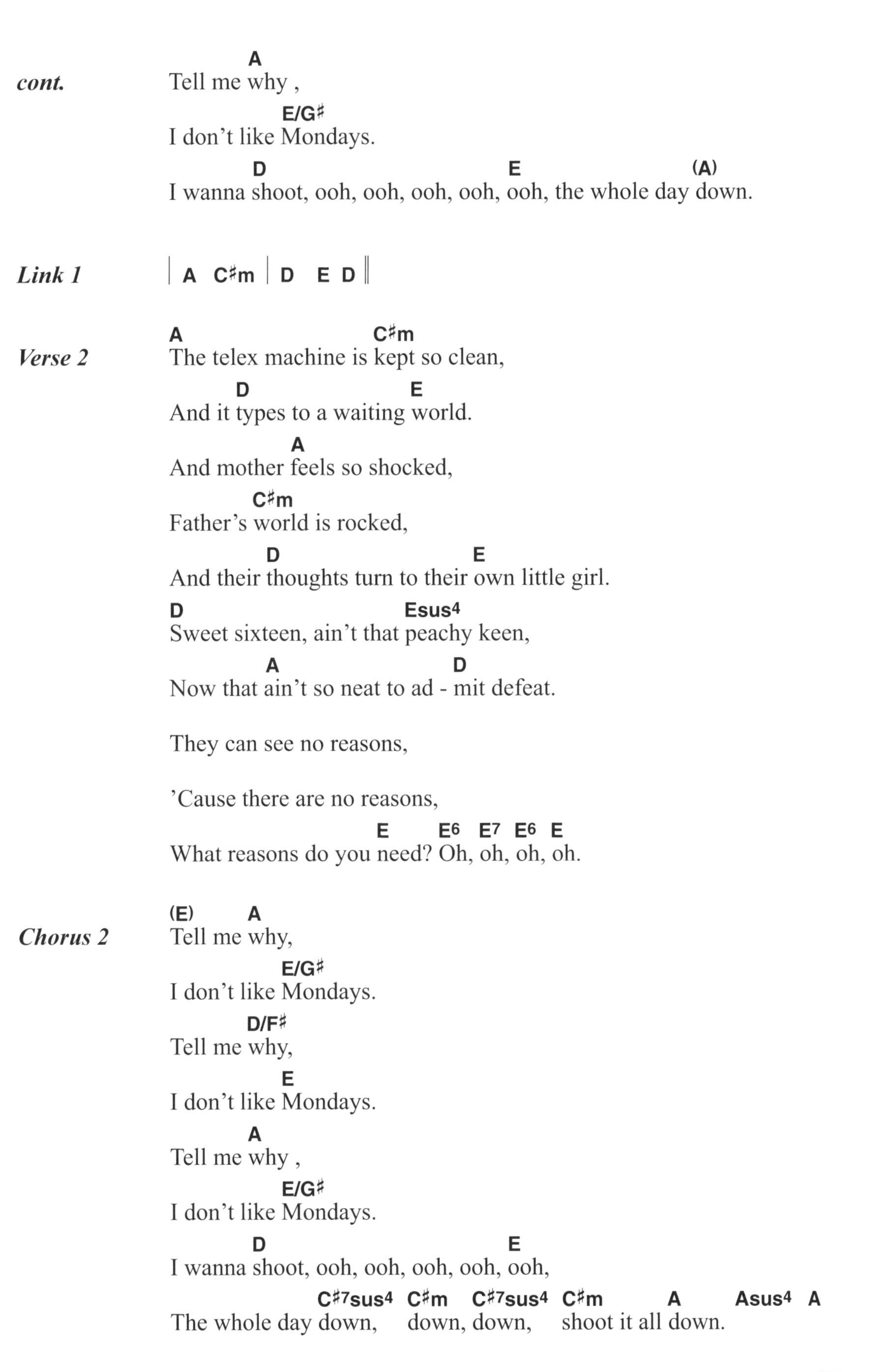

cont.

A
Tell me why ,
E/G♯
I don't like Mondays.
D E (A)
I wanna shoot, ooh, ooh, ooh, ooh, ooh, the whole day down.

Link 1 | A C♯m | D E D ||

Verse 2

A C♯m
The telex machine is kept so clean,
D E
And it types to a waiting world.
A
And mother feels so shocked,
C♯m
Father's world is rocked,
D E
And their thoughts turn to their own little girl.
D Esus4
Sweet sixteen, ain't that peachy keen,
A D
Now that ain't so neat to ad - mit defeat.

They can see no reasons,

'Cause there are no reasons,
E E6 E7 E6 E
What reasons do you need? Oh, oh, oh, oh.

Chorus 2

(E) A
Tell me why,
E/G♯
I don't like Mondays.
D/F♯
Tell me why,
E
I don't like Mondays.
A
Tell me why ,
E/G♯
I don't like Mondays.
D E
I wanna shoot, ooh, ooh, ooh, ooh, ooh,
C♯7sus4 C♯m C♯7sus4 C♯m A Asus4 A
The whole day down, down, down, shoot it all down.

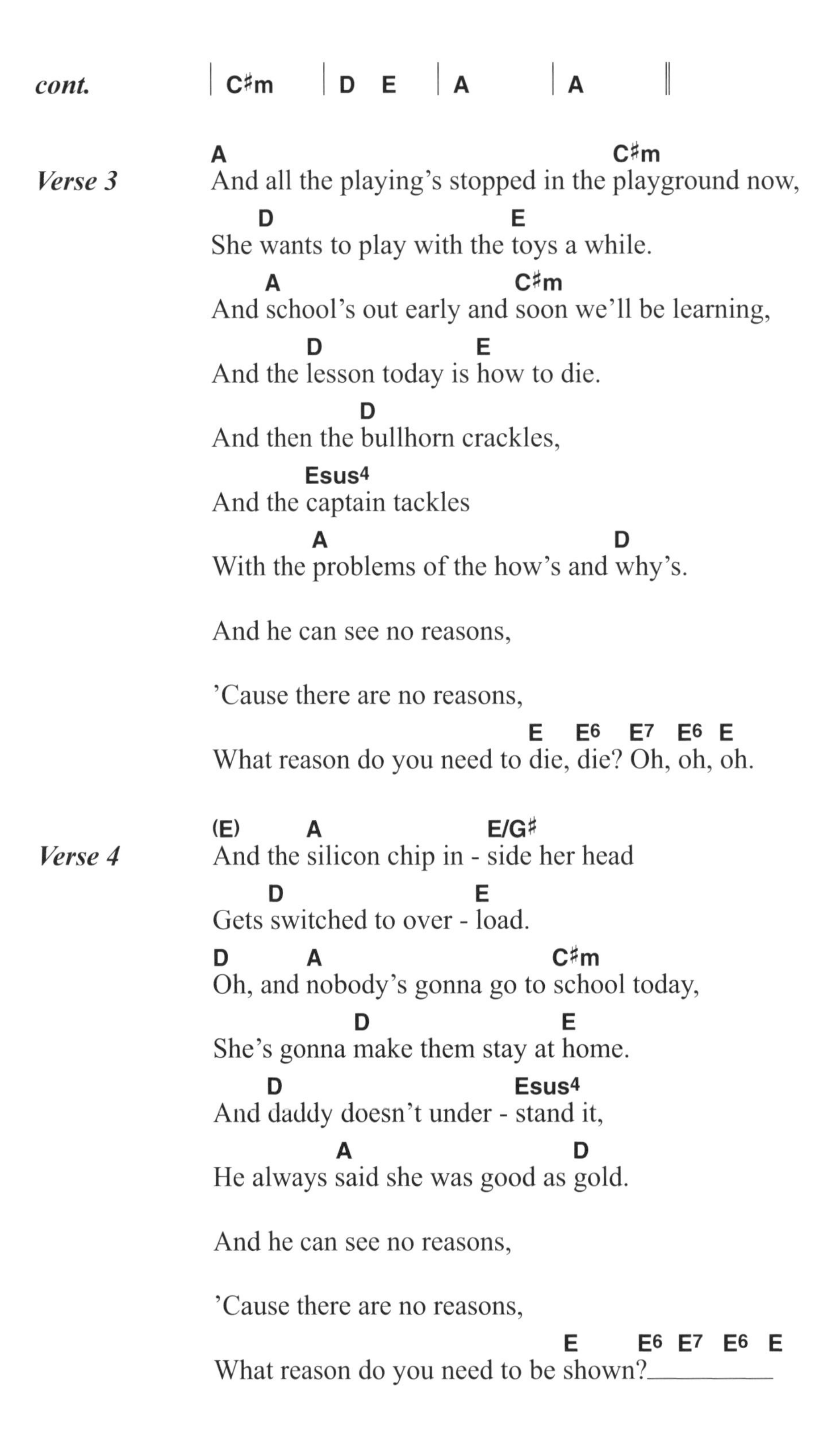

cont. | C♯m | D E | A | A ||

Verse 3

A C♯m
And all the playing's stopped in the playground now,
D E
She wants to play with the toys a while.
A C♯m
And school's out early and soon we'll be learning,
D E
And the lesson today is how to die.
D
And then the bullhorn crackles,
Esus4
And the captain tackles
A D
With the problems of the how's and why's.

And he can see no reasons,

'Cause there are no reasons,
E E6 E7 E6 E
What reason do you need to die, die? Oh, oh, oh.

Verse 4

(E) A E/G♯
And the silicon chip in - side her head
D E
Gets switched to over - load.
D A C♯m
Oh, and nobody's gonna go to school today,
D E
She's gonna make them stay at home.
D Esus4
And daddy doesn't under - stand it,
A D
He always said she was good as gold.

And he can see no reasons,

'Cause there are no reasons,
E E6 E7 E6 E
What reason do you need to be shown?________

Chorus 3

(E)   A
Tell me why,

             E/G♯
I don't like Mondays.

         D/F♯
Tell me why,

             E
I don't like Mondays.

         A
Tell me why,

I don't like,

 E/G♯   D
I don't like, (tell me why)

             E
I don't like Mondays.

         A
Tell me why,

I don't like,

 C♯m   D
I don't like, (tell me why)

             E
I don't like Mondays.

         A
Tell me why,

             C♯m
I don't like Mondays.

         D   E
I wanna shoot, ooh, ooh, ooh, ooh, ooh,

                 A
The whole day down.

C♯m   D   E   A
Ooh, ooh, ooh, ooh, ooh, ooh, ooh.

I Useta Lover

Words & Music by Leo Moran, Paul Cunniffe, Dave Carton & Padraig Stevens

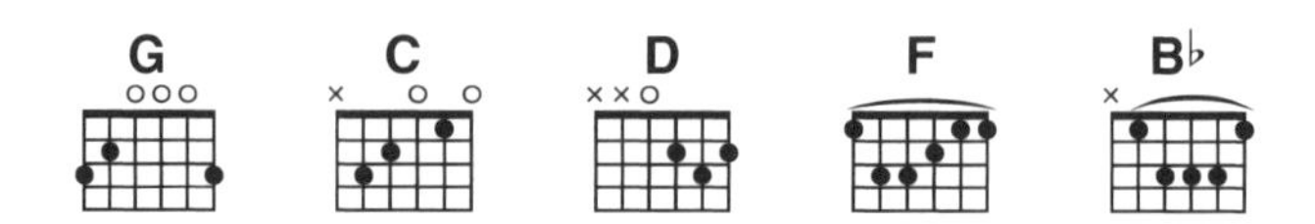

Verse 1

```
            G                                          C
I have fallen for another, she can make her own way home.
                                         G
And even if she asked me now I'd let her go a - lone.
                                                   C
I useta see her up the chapel when she went to Sunday mass,
And when she'd go to receive,
                                 G
I'd kneel down there and watch her pass,
                 D
The glory of her ass.
```

Chorus 1

```
G                              C
I useta love her, I useta love her once,
A long, long time ago.
G                             C
I useta love her, I useta love her once,
A long long time ago.
     F     B♭          C
It's gone, all my lovin' is gone.
                 F      B♭           C
Whoa, whoa, it's gone, all my lovin' is gone.
```

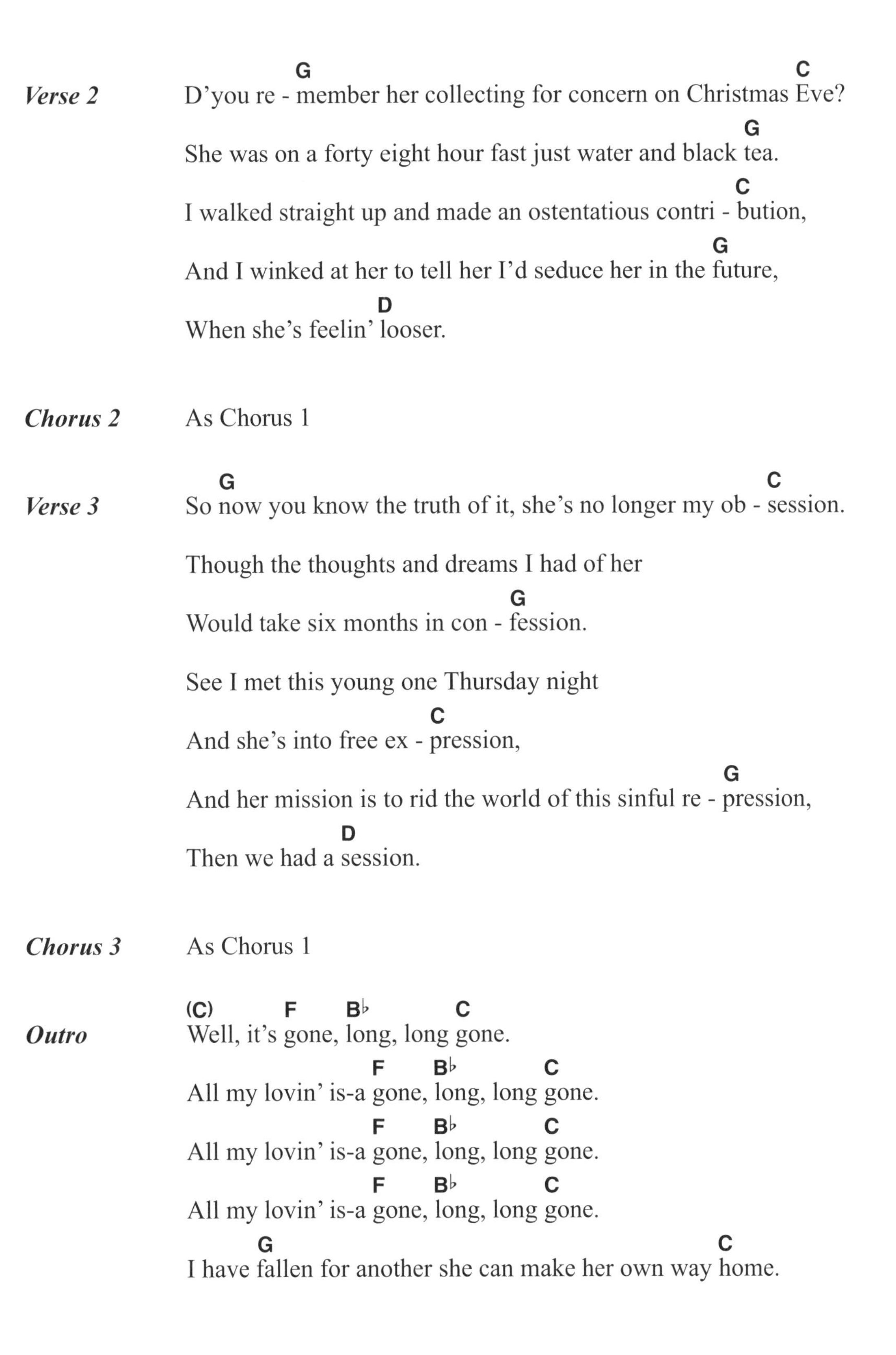

Verse 2

G C
D'you re - member her collecting for concern on Christmas Eve?

G
She was on a forty eight hour fast just water and black tea.

C
I walked straight up and made an ostentatious contri - bution,

G
And I winked at her to tell her I'd seduce her in the future,

D
When she's feelin' looser.

Chorus 2

As Chorus 1

Verse 3

G C
So now you know the truth of it, she's no longer my ob - session.

Though the thoughts and dreams I had of her

G
Would take six months in con - fession.

See I met this young one Thursday night

C
And she's into free ex - pression,

G
And her mission is to rid the world of this sinful re - pression,

D
Then we had a session.

Chorus 3

As Chorus 1

Outro

(C) F B♭ C
Well, it's gone, long, long gone.

F B♭ C
All my lovin' is-a gone, long, long gone.

F B♭ C
All my lovin' is-a gone, long, long gone.

F B♭ C
All my lovin' is-a gone, long, long gone.

G C
I have fallen for another she can make her own way home.

Irish Heartbeat

Words & Music by Van Morrison

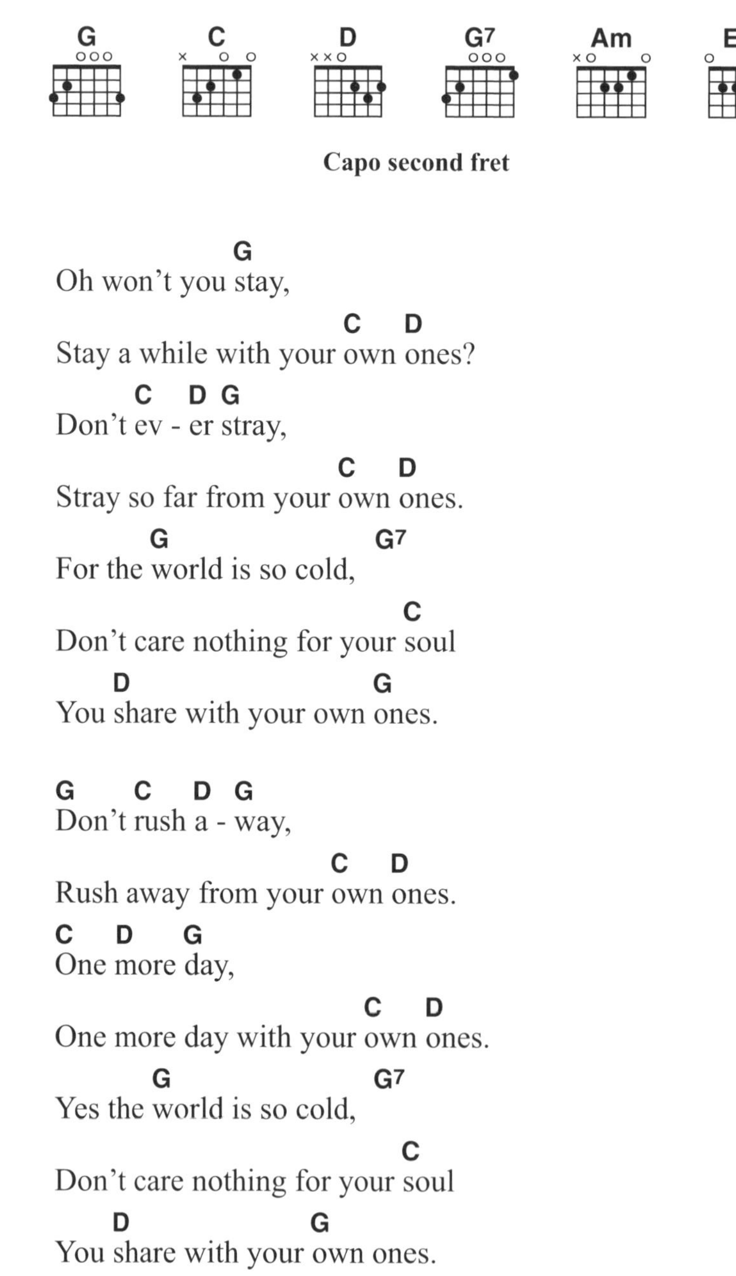

Verse 1

Verse 2

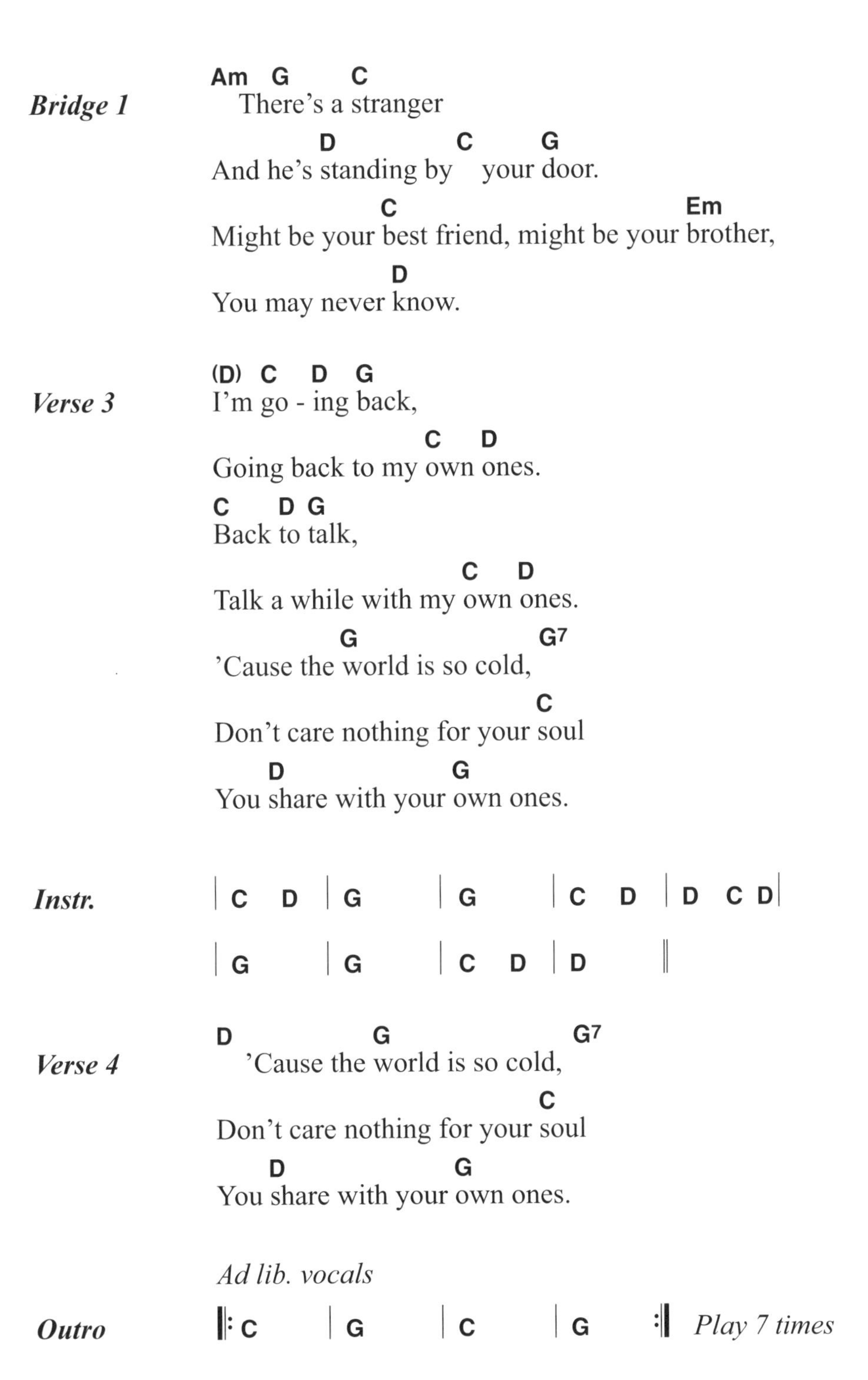

Bridge 1

```
Am   G      C
   There's a stranger
              D              C        G
And he's standing by     your door.
                     C                              Em
Might be your best friend, might be your brother,
                      D
You may never know.
```

Verse 3

```
(D) C   D   G
I'm go - ing back,
                           C    D
Going back to my own ones.
C     D G
Back to talk,
                              C    D
Talk a while with my own ones.
               G                  G7
'Cause the world is so cold,
                                      C
Don't care nothing for your soul
     D                 G
You share with your own ones.
```

Instr.

```
| C   D | G      | G      | C   D | D  C D |
| G     | G      | C   D  | D      ||
```

Verse 4

```
D               G                  G7
   'Cause the world is so cold,
                                      C
Don't care nothing for your soul
     D                 G
You share with your own ones.
```

Ad lib. vocals

Outro

```
||: C     | G     | C     | G     :|| Play 7 times
```

In A Lifetime

Words & Music by Ciarán Brennan & Pól Brennan

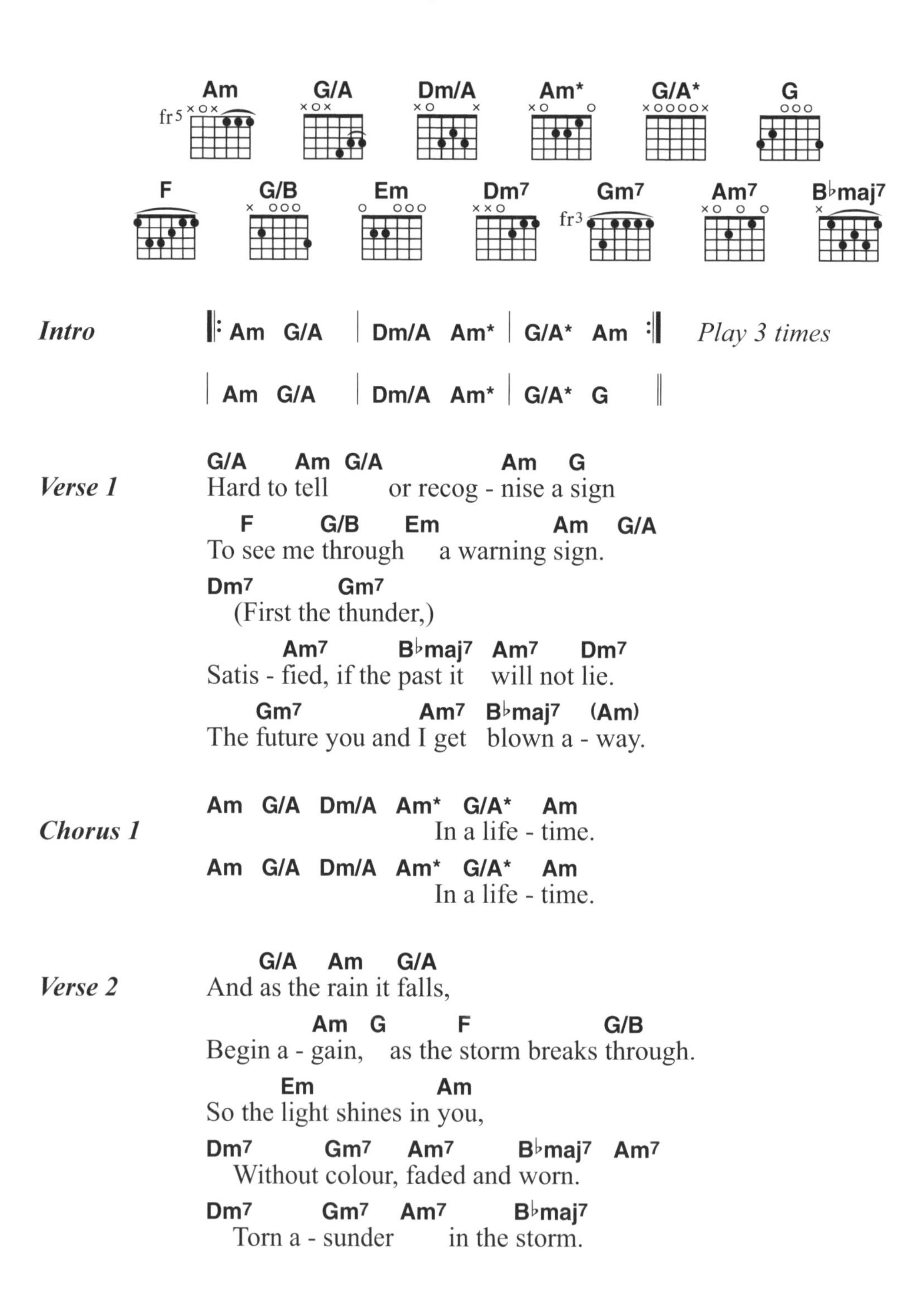

```
Instr.        | Am7   G  | F   G    | Am7   G  | F   G    ||

                 Dm7      Gm7        Am7                   B♭maj7   Am7
Bridge 1      Un - less the sound has saved your body's soul,
              Dm7       Gm7   Am7       B♭maj7   Am7
                Unless        it disap - pears.
              Dm7        Gm7    Am7        B♭maj7    Am7
                Selfish storms hold on the inside,
              Dm7    Gm7  Am7       B♭maj7
                One life        in the storm.


Chorus 2      Am   G/A   Dm/A   Am*   G/A*   Am

              Am   G/A   Dm/A   Am*   G/A*   Am
                                   In a life - time.
              Am   G/A   Dm/A   Am*   G/A*   Am
                                   In a life - time.
              Am   G/A   Dm/A   Am*   G/A*   Am
                                   In a life - time.
              Am   G/A   Dm/A   Am*   G/A*   Am
                                   In a life - time.


Outro         ||: Am   G/A   | Dm/A   Am* | G/A*   Am :||   Repeat to fade
```

Have I Told You Lately

Words & Music by Van Morrison

F♯m11 B11 Eadd9 G♯m7 Amaj7

Intro

| F♯m11 | B11 |

| Eadd9 G♯m7 | Amaj7 B11 | Eadd9 G♯m7 | Amaj7 B11 |

| Amaj7 | G♯m7 | F♯m11 B11 | Eadd9 B11 ||
(Have I)

Chorus 1

```
(B11)  Eadd9   G♯m7          Amaj7       B11
Have I told you lately that I love you?
Eadd9              G♯m7                 Amaj7         B11   Amaj7
   Have I told you there's no one a - bove you?
                                  G♯m7
Fill my heart with gladness,
                                  F♯m11
Take away my sadness and
             B11                                Eadd9    B11
Ease my troubles, that's what you do.
```

Verse 1

```
Eadd9              G♯m7                  Amaj7   B11
   Oh the morn - ing   sun in all its glory,
Eadd9              G♯m7                          Amaj7   B11   Amaj7
   Greets the day with hope and comfort too.
                                             G♯m7
And you fill my life with laughter,
                              F♯m11
You can make it better,
             B11                              Eadd9     F♯m11   G♯m7
Ease my troubles that's what you do.
```

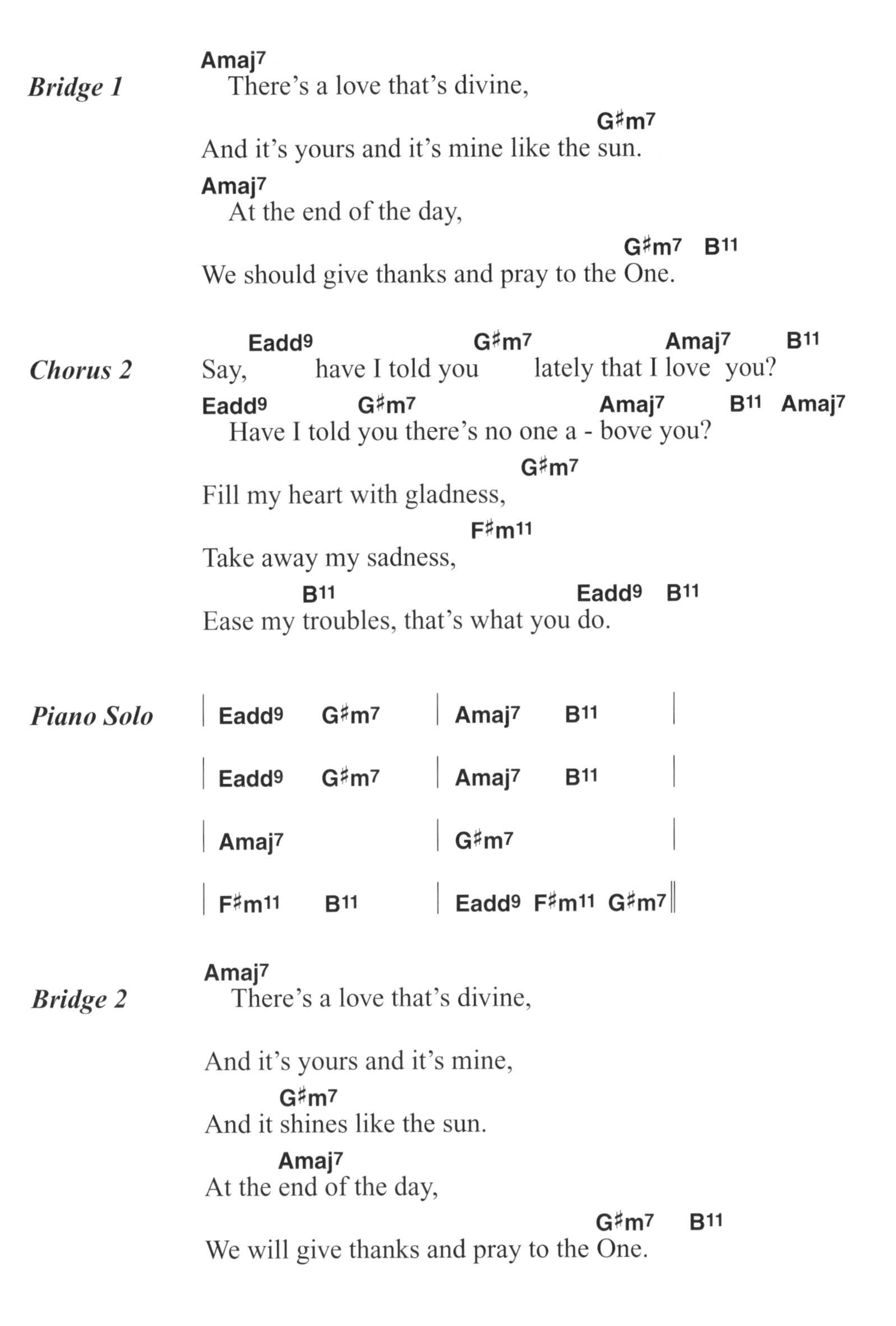

Bridge 1

Amaj7
There's a love that's divine,
G♯m7
And it's yours and it's mine like the sun.
Amaj7
At the end of the day,
G♯m7 B11
We should give thanks and pray to the One.

Chorus 2

Eadd9 G♯m7 Amaj7 B11
Say, have I told you lately that I love you?
Eadd9 G♯m7 Amaj7 B11 Amaj7
Have I told you there's no one a - bove you?
G♯m7
Fill my heart with gladness,
F♯m11
Take away my sadness,
B11 Eadd9 B11
Ease my troubles, that's what you do.

Piano Solo

Eadd9 G♯m7	Amaj7 B11
Eadd9 G♯m7	Amaj7 B11
Amaj7	G♯m7
F♯m11 B11	Eadd9 F♯m11 G♯m7	

Bridge 2

Amaj7
There's a love that's divine,
And it's yours and it's mine,
G♯m7
And it shines like the sun.
Amaj7
At the end of the day,
G♯m7 B11
We will give thanks and pray to the One.

Chorus 3

(B11) Eadd9 G♯m7 Amaj7 B11
Have I told you lately that I love you?

Eadd9 G♯m7 Amaj7 B11 Amaj7
Have I told you there's no one above you?

G♯m7
Fill my heart with gladness,

F♯m11
Take away my sadness and

B11 Eadd9 F♯m11 G♯m7
Ease my troubles, that's what you do.

Outro

Amaj7 G♯m7
Take away my sadness,

F♯m11
Fill my life with gladness yeah,

B11 Eadd9 F♯m11 G♯m7 Amaj7
Ease my troubles that's what you do.

G♯m7
Fill my life with gladness,

F♯m11
Take away my sadness,

B11 Eadd9
Ease my troubles that's what you do.

Life Is A Rollercoaster

Words & Music by Gregg Alexander & Rick Nowels

C G Dm7 Am7 Fmaj7 Em F/G B♭

Intro

                                    C   G
Na, na, na, na, na.
                                    Dm7
Na, na, na, na, na.
                                    C   G
Na, na, na, na, na.
                                    Dm7
Na, na, na, na, na.

Verse 1

(Dm7) C   G
   Hey baby,
                                        Dm7
You really got my tail in a spin.
      C   G
Hey baby,
                                        Dm7
I don't even know where to begin.
     Am7   G   Fmaj7   Em
But baby I got one thing I want you to know,
          Am7   G   F/G   G
Where - ever you go, tell me 'cause I'm gonna go.

Chorus 1

(G)   C   G   Dm7
We found love,   so don't fight it.
C   G   Dm7
Life is a roller - coaster, just gotta ride it.
        C   G   Dm7
I need you,   so stop hiding,
     C   G   Dm7
Our love is a myste - ry girl, let's get in - side it.

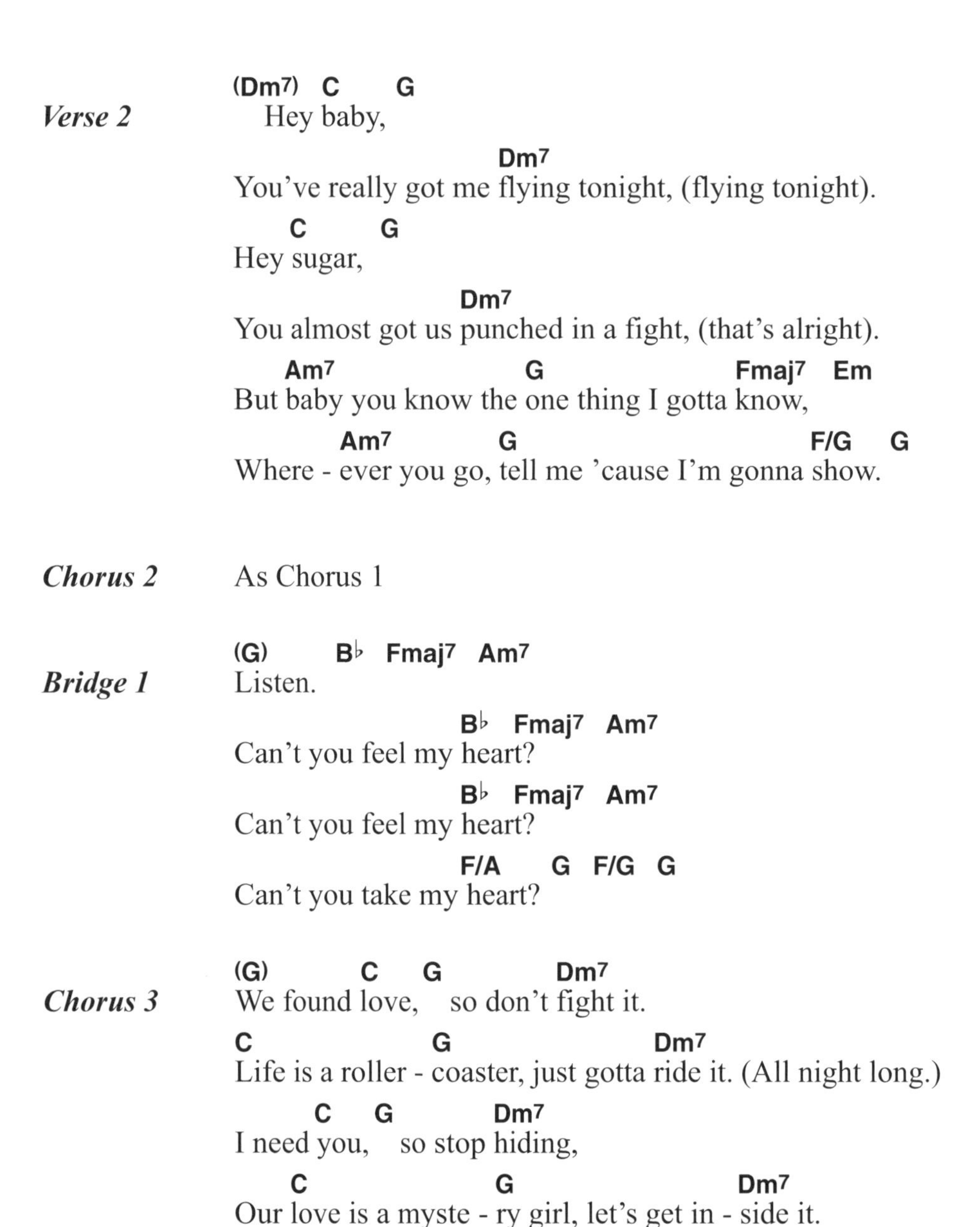

Verse 2

(Dm7) C G
Hey baby,

Dm7
You've really got me flying tonight, (flying tonight).

C G
Hey sugar,

Dm7
You almost got us punched in a fight, (that's alright).

Am7 G Fmaj7 Em
But baby you know the one thing I gotta know,

Am7 G F/G G
Where - ever you go, tell me 'cause I'm gonna show.

Chorus 2

As Chorus 1

Bridge 1

(G) B♭ Fmaj7 Am7
Listen.

B♭ Fmaj7 Am7
Can't you feel my heart?

B♭ Fmaj7 Am7
Can't you feel my heart?

F/A G F/G G
Can't you take my heart?

Chorus 3

(G) C G Dm7
We found love, so don't fight it.

C G Dm7
Life is a roller - coaster, just gotta ride it. (All night long.)

C G Dm7
I need you, so stop hiding,

C G Dm7
Our love is a myste - ry girl, let's get in - side it.

```
                C                 G
Outro   Don't fight it, fight it, fight it.
              Dm7
        Don't fight it, fight it, fight it.
              C                 G
        Don't fight it, fight it, fight it.
              Dm7
        Don't fight it, fight it, fight it.
              C                 G
        Don't fight it, fight it, fight it.
                         Dm7
        Na, na, na, na, na.
                         C
        Na, na, na, na, na.
                                G                     Dm7
        Our love is a myste - ry girl, let's get in - side it.   To fade
```

Linger

Words by Dolores O'Riordan
Music by Dolores O'Riordan & Noel Hogan

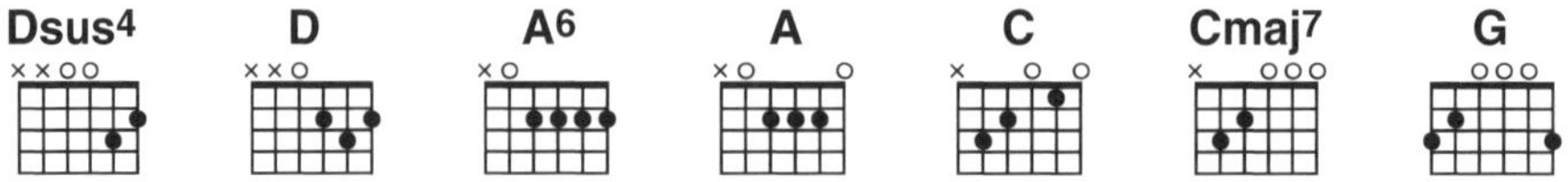

Dsus4 D A6 A C Cmaj7 G

Intro

```
||: Dsus4 | D | Dsus4 | D :|| Dsus4 ||
| A6  A | A6 | C  Cmaj7 | C  Cmaj7 | G | G ||
```

Verse 1

```
 D
If you, if you could return,
            A6
Don't let it burn, don't let it fade.
                      C
I'm sure I'm not being rude,

But it's just your attitude,
                  G
It's tearing me apart,

It's ruining ev'rything.
```

Verse 2

```
 D
I swore, I swore I would be true,
                   A6
And honey, so did you,
                             C
So why were you holding her hand?

Is that the way we stand?
                      G
Were you lying all the time?

Was it just a game to you?
```

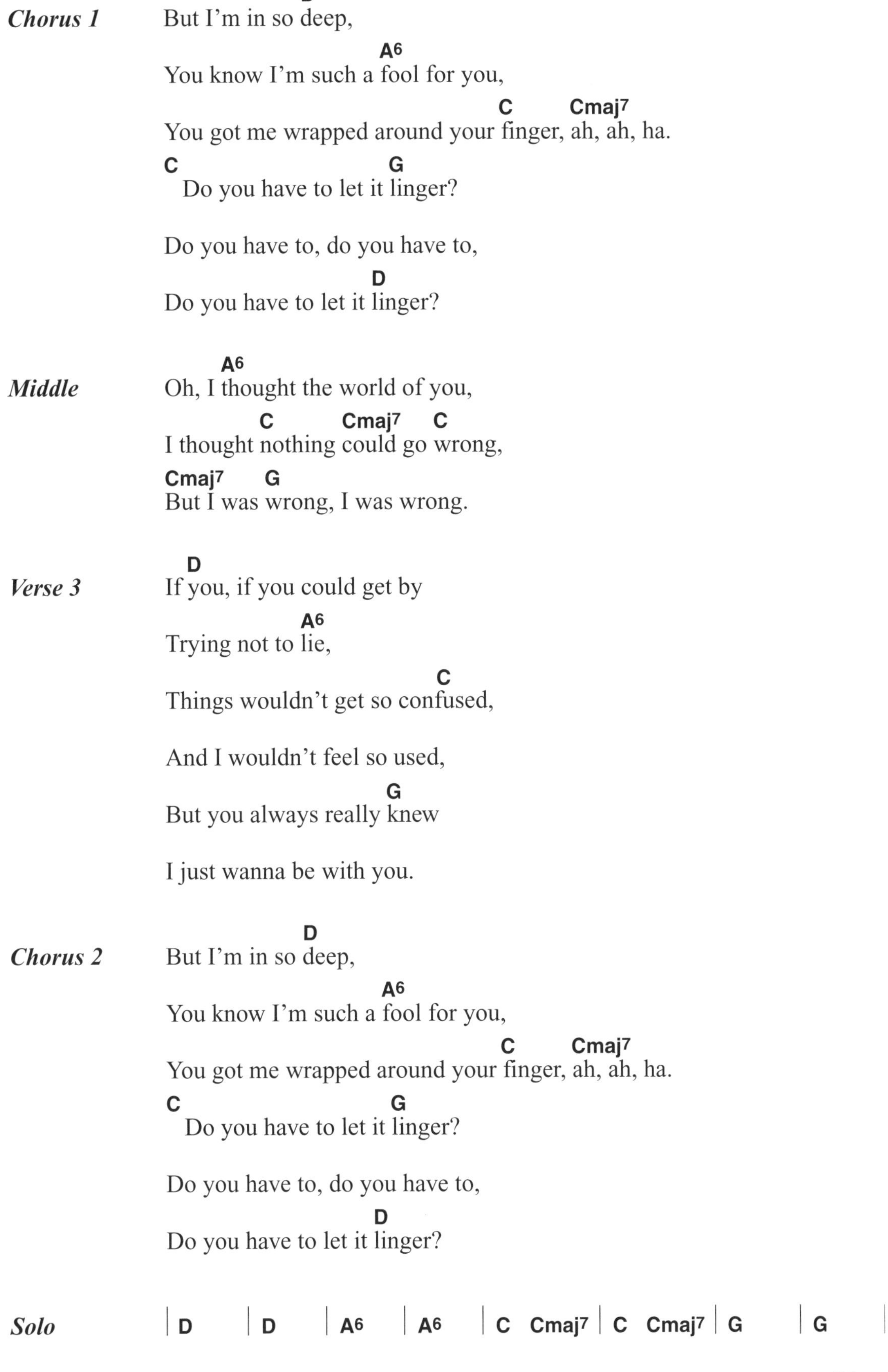

Chorus 1

D
But I'm in so deep,
A6
You know I'm such a fool for you,
C Cmaj7
You got me wrapped around your finger, ah, ah, ha.
C G
Do you have to let it linger?
Do you have to, do you have to,
D
Do you have to let it linger?

Middle

A6
Oh, I thought the world of you,
C Cmaj7 C
I thought nothing could go wrong,
Cmaj7 G
But I was wrong, I was wrong.

Verse 3

D
If you, if you could get by
A6
Trying not to lie,
C
Things wouldn't get so confused,
And I wouldn't feel so used,
G
But you always really knew
I just wanna be with you.

Chorus 2

D
But I'm in so deep,
A6
You know I'm such a fool for you,
C Cmaj7
You got me wrapped around your finger, ah, ah, ha.
C G
Do you have to let it linger?
Do you have to, do you have to,
D
Do you have to let it linger?

Solo

| D | D | A6 | A6 | C Cmaj7 | C Cmaj7 | G | G |

Chorus 3

```
                D
But I'm in so deep,
                         A6
You know I'm such a fool for you,
                                     C       Cmaj7
You got me wrapped around your finger, ah, ah, ha.
C                       G
   Do you have to let it linger?

Do you have to, do you have to,
                           D
Do you have to let it linger?
```

Chorus 4

```
                         A6
You know I'm such a fool for you,
                                     C       Cmaj7
You got me wrapped around your finger, ah, ah, ha.
C                       G
   Do you have to let it linger?

Do you have to, do you have to,
                           D
Do you have to let it linger?
```

Instrumental

```
| D     | D     | A6    | A6    | C  Cmaj7 | C  Cmaj7 | G     | G     |
| D     | D  Dsus4 | D     | D  Dsus4 | D     | D  Dsus4 | D     ||
```

The Man Who Can't Be Moved

Words & Music by
Andrew Frampton, Steve Kipner, Mark Sheehan & Daniel O'Donoghue

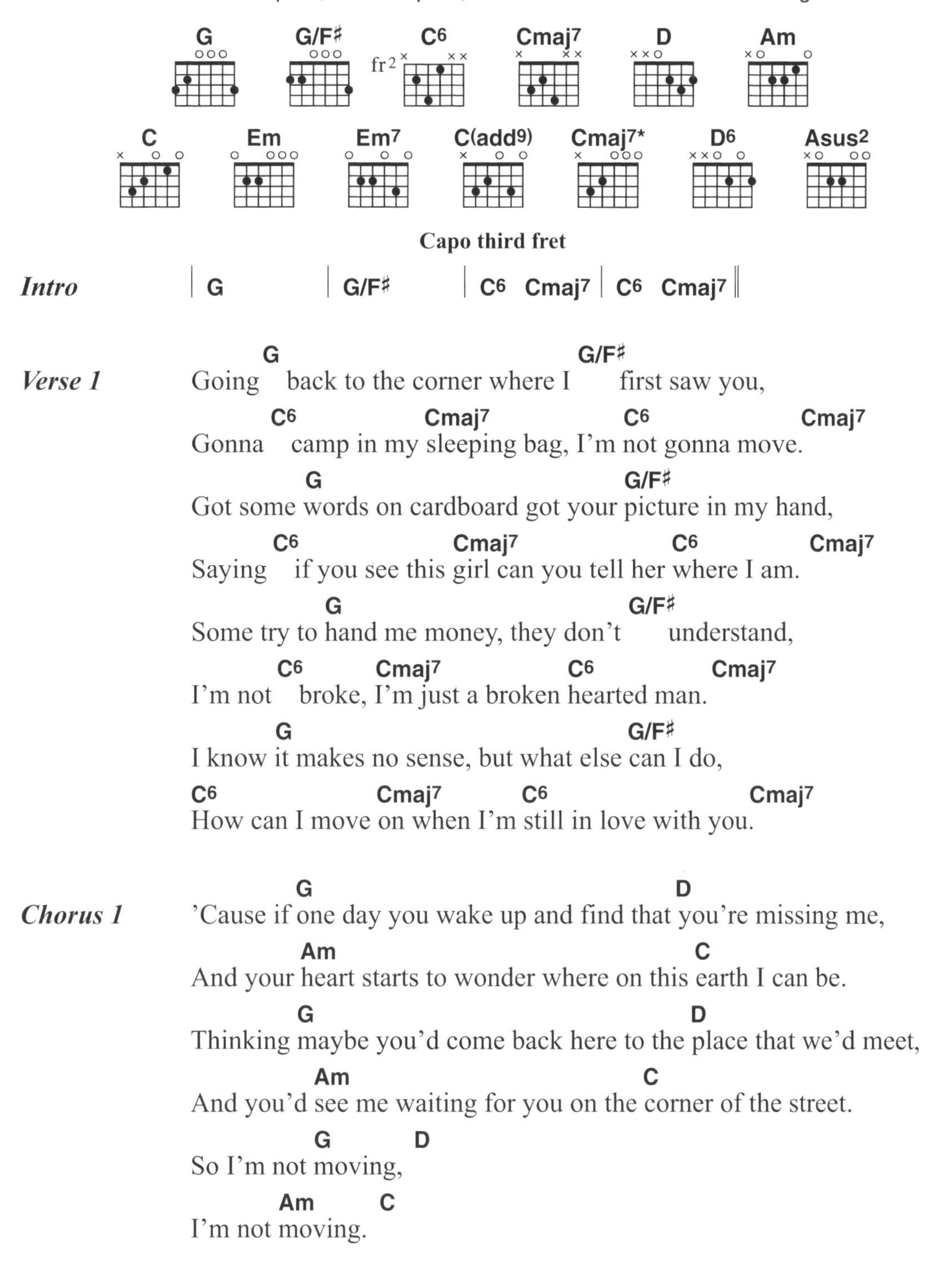

Capo third fret

Intro | G | G/F♯ | C6 Cmaj7 | C6 Cmaj7 ||

Verse 1

G G/F♯
Going back to the corner where I first saw you,
C6 Cmaj7 C6 Cmaj7
Gonna camp in my sleeping bag, I'm not gonna move.
G G/F♯
Got some words on cardboard got your picture in my hand,
C6 Cmaj7 C6 Cmaj7
Saying if you see this girl can you tell her where I am.
G G/F♯
Some try to hand me money, they don't understand,
C6 Cmaj7 C6 Cmaj7
I'm not broke, I'm just a broken hearted man.
G G/F♯
I know it makes no sense, but what else can I do,
C6 Cmaj7 C6 Cmaj7
How can I move on when I'm still in love with you.

Chorus 1

G D
'Cause if one day you wake up and find that you're missing me,
Am C
And your heart starts to wonder where on this earth I can be.
G D
Thinking maybe you'd come back here to the place that we'd meet,
Am C
And you'd see me waiting for you on the corner of the street.
G D
So I'm not moving,
Am C
I'm not moving.

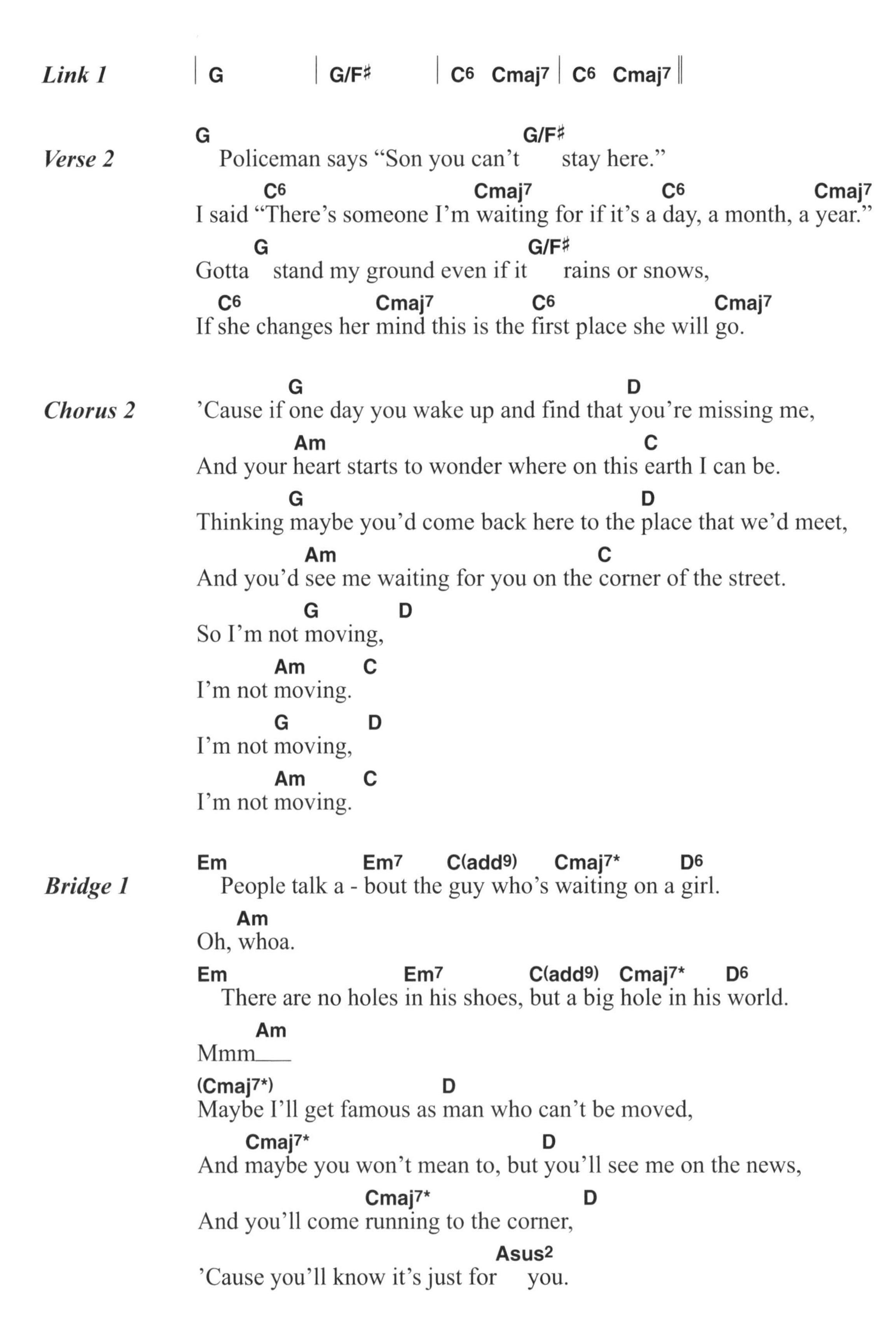

Link 1 | G | G/F♯ | C6 Cmaj7 | C6 Cmaj7 ||

Verse 2

G G/F♯
Policeman says "Son you can't stay here."

C6 Cmaj7 C6 Cmaj7
I said "There's someone I'm waiting for if it's a day, a month, a year."

G G/F♯
Gotta stand my ground even if it rains or snows,

C6 Cmaj7 C6 Cmaj7
If she changes her mind this is the first place she will go.

Chorus 2

G D
'Cause if one day you wake up and find that you're missing me,

Am C
And your heart starts to wonder where on this earth I can be.

G D
Thinking maybe you'd come back here to the place that we'd meet,

Am C
And you'd see me waiting for you on the corner of the street.

G D
So I'm not moving,

Am C
I'm not moving.

G D
I'm not moving,

Am C
I'm not moving.

Bridge 1

Em Em7 C(add9) Cmaj7* D6
People talk a - bout the guy who's waiting on a girl.

Am
Oh, whoa.

Em Em7 C(add9) Cmaj7* D6
There are no holes in his shoes, but a big hole in his world.

Am
Mmm___

(Cmaj7*) D
Maybe I'll get famous as man who can't be moved,

Cmaj7* D
And maybe you won't mean to, but you'll see me on the news,

Cmaj7* D
And you'll come running to the corner,

Asus2
'Cause you'll know it's just for you.

cont. I'm the man who can't be moved,

```
                 C
I'm the man    who can't be moved.
```

Chorus 3

```
            G                                         D
'Cause if one day you wake up and find that you're missing me,
            Am                                          C
And your heart starts to wonder where on this earth I can be.
            G                                       D
Thinking maybe you'd come back here to the place that we'd meet,
              Am                                    C
And you'd see me waiting for you on the corner of the street.
              G          D
So I'm not moving,
          Am        C
I'm not moving.
          G         D
I'm not moving,
          Am        C
I'm not moving.
```

Outro

```
         G                                 G/F#
Going    back to the corner where I        first saw you,
          G6               Cmaj7              C6                   Cmaj7
Gonna     camp in my sleeping bag, I'm not gonna move.
```

Nothing Compares 2 U

Words & Music by Prince

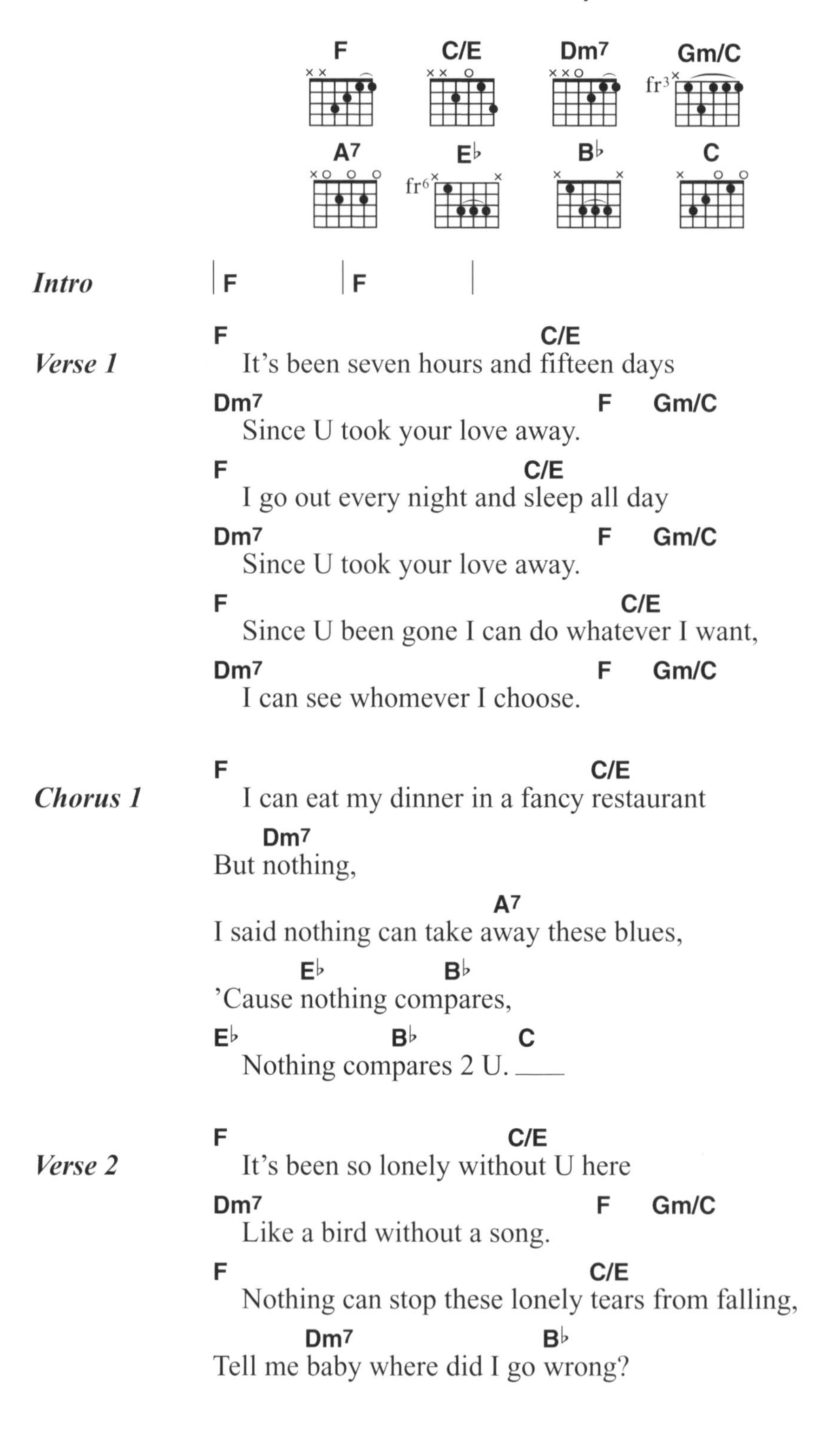

Intro | F | F |

Verse 1

F C/E
It's been seven hours and fifteen days
Dm7 F Gm/C
Since U took your love away.
F C/E
I go out every night and sleep all day
Dm7 F Gm/C
Since U took your love away.
F C/E
Since U been gone I can do whatever I want,
Dm7 F Gm/C
I can see whomever I choose.

Chorus 1

F C/E
I can eat my dinner in a fancy restaurant
Dm7
But nothing,
A7
I said nothing can take away these blues,
E♭ B♭
'Cause nothing compares,
E♭ B♭ C
Nothing compares 2 U. ___

Verse 2

F C/E
It's been so lonely without U here
Dm7 F Gm/C
Like a bird without a song.
F C/E
Nothing can stop these lonely tears from falling,
Dm7 B♭
Tell me baby where did I go wrong?

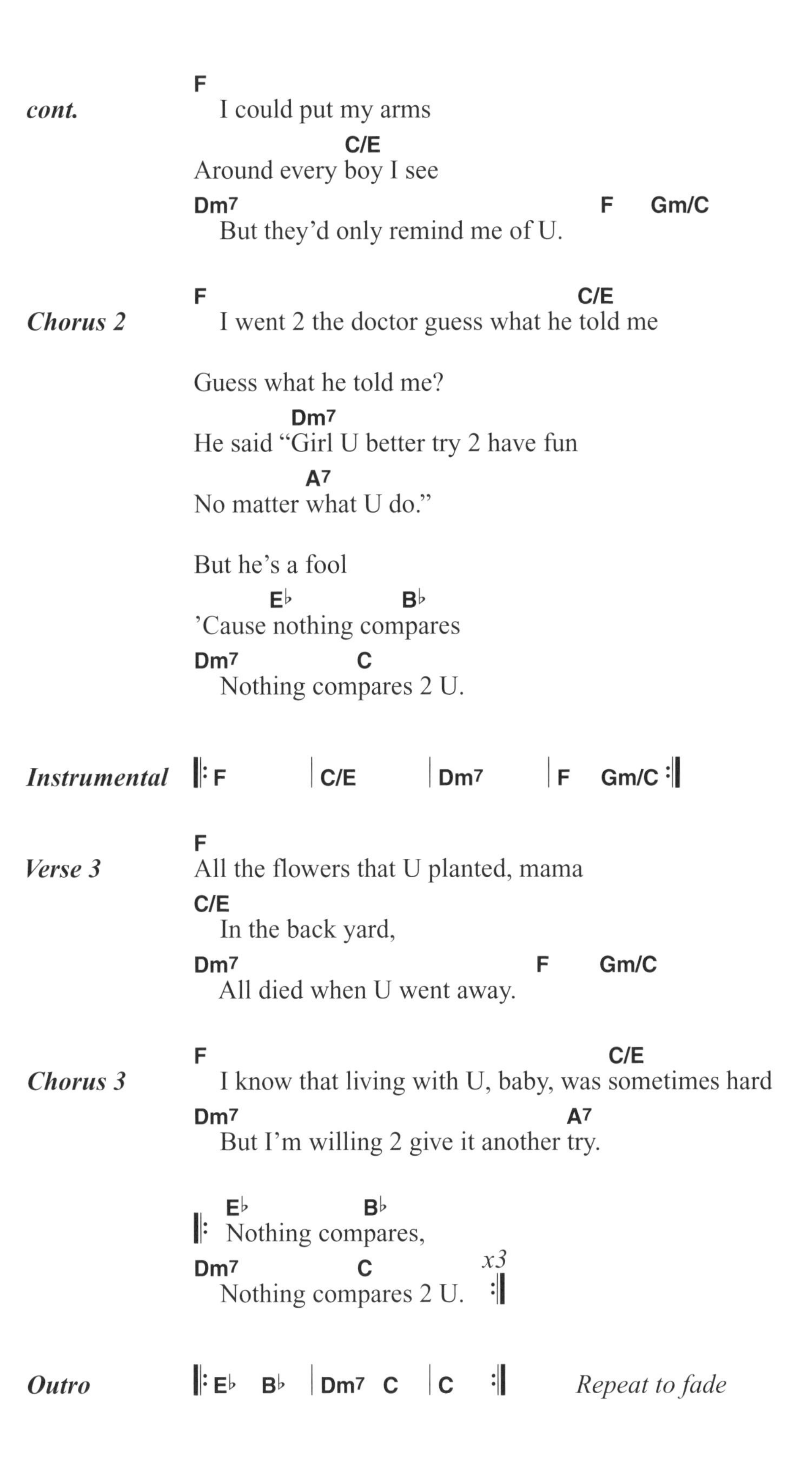
cont.
F
I could put my arms
C/E
Around every boy I see
Dm7 F Gm/C
But they'd only remind me of U.
Chorus 2
F C/E
I went 2 the doctor guess what he told me
Guess what he told me?
Dm7
He said "Girl U better try 2 have fun
A7
No matter what U do."
But he's a fool
E♭ B♭
'Cause nothing compares
Dm7 C
Nothing compares 2 U.
Instrumental
F | C/E | Dm7 | F Gm/C
Verse 3
F
All the flowers that U planted, mama
C/E
In the back yard,
Dm7 F Gm/C
All died when U went away.
Chorus 3
F C/E
I know that living with U, baby, was sometimes hard
Dm7 A7
But I'm willing 2 give it another try.
E♭ B♭
Nothing compares,
Dm7 C
Nothing compares 2 U.
x3
Outro
E♭ B♭ | Dm7 C | C
Repeat to fade

One

Words & Music by U2

Am D Fmaj7 G C

Intro

| Am | D | Fmaj7 | G ||

Verse 1

Am D
Is it getting better,
Fmaj7 G
Or do you feel the same?
Am D
Will it make it easier on you,
Fmaj7 G
Now you got someone to blame?

Chorus 1

C Am
You say one love, one life,
Fmaj7 C
When it's one need in the night.
Am
One love, we get to share it,
Fmaj7 C
Leaves you baby if you don't care for it.

| Am | D | Fmaj7 | G ||

Verse 2

Am D
Did I disappoint you,
Fmaj7 G
Or leave a bad taste in your mouth?
Am D
You act like you never had love
Fmaj7 G
And you want me to go without.

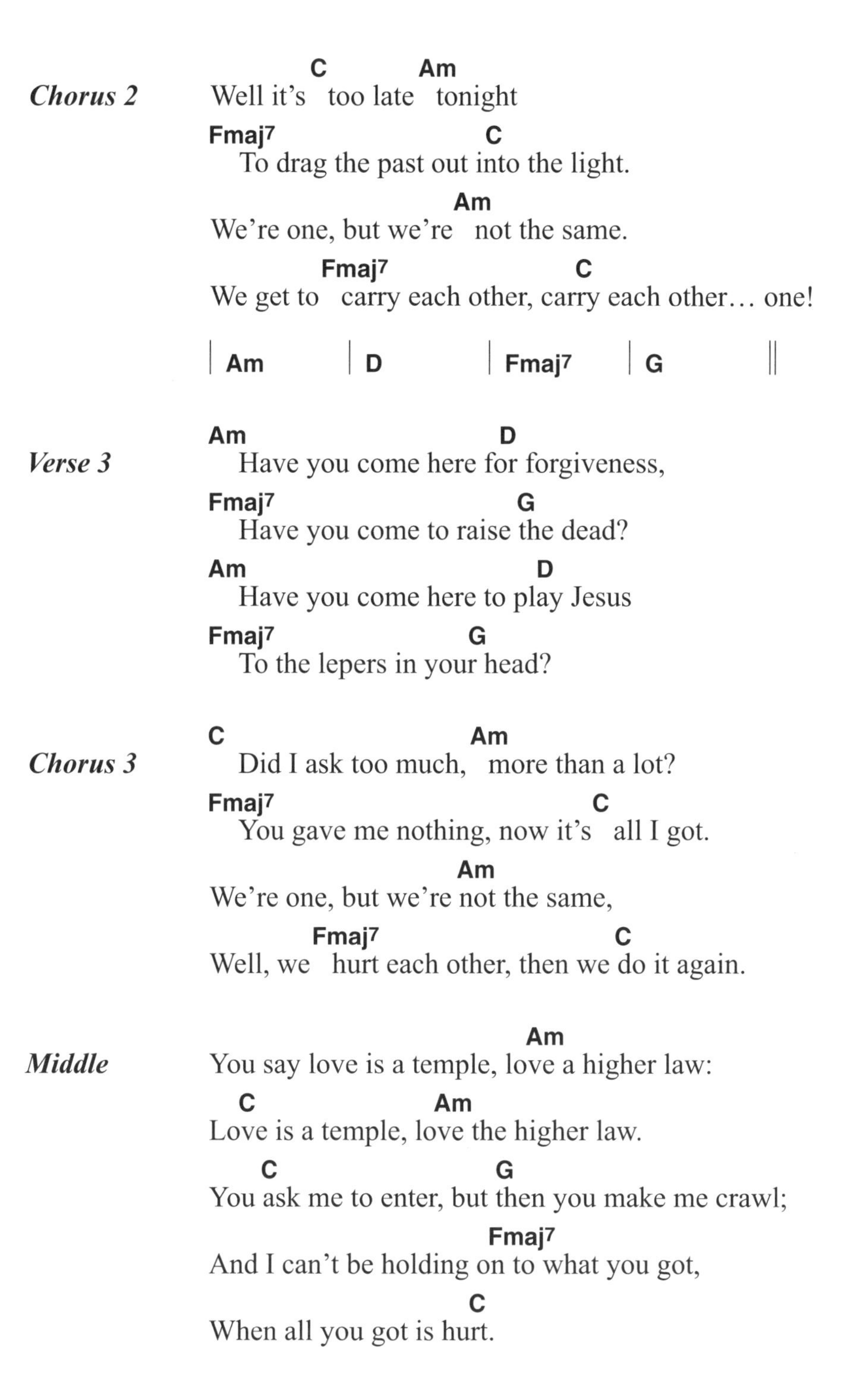

Chorus 2

C Am
Well it's too late tonight
Fmaj7 C
To drag the past out into the light.
Am
We're one, but we're not the same.
Fmaj7 C
We get to carry each other, carry each other… one!

| Am | D | Fmaj7 | G ||

Verse 3

Am D
Have you come here for forgiveness,
Fmaj7 G
Have you come to raise the dead?
Am D
Have you come here to play Jesus
Fmaj7 G
To the lepers in your head?

Chorus 3

C Am
Did I ask too much, more than a lot?
Fmaj7 C
You gave me nothing, now it's all I got.
Am
We're one, but we're not the same,
Fmaj7 C
Well, we hurt each other, then we do it again.

Middle

Am
You say love is a temple, love a higher law:
C Am
Love is a temple, love the higher law.
C G
You ask me to enter, but then you make me crawl;
Fmaj7
And I can't be holding on to what you got,
C
When all you got is hurt.

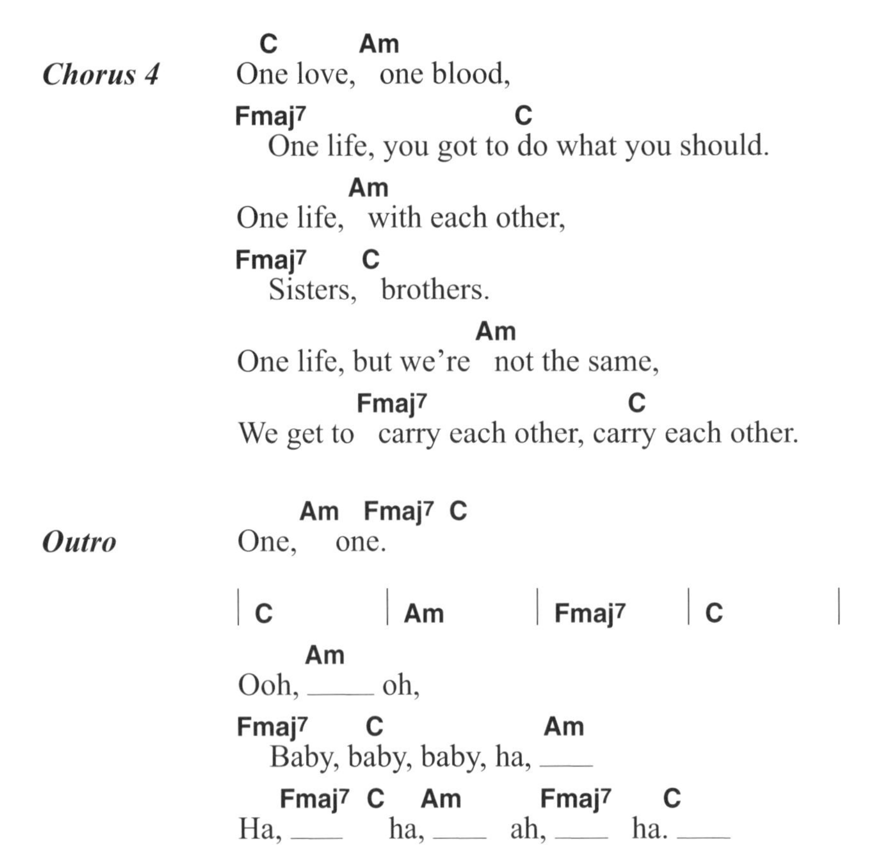
Chorus 4
C Am
One love, one blood,
Fmaj7 C
One life, you got to do what you should.
Am
One life, with each other,
Fmaj7 C
Sisters, brothers.
Am
One life, but we're not the same,
Fmaj7 C
We get to carry each other, carry each other.
Outro
Am Fmaj7 C
One, one.
| C | Am | Fmaj7 | C |
Am
Ooh, ___ oh,
Fmaj7 C Am
Baby, baby, baby, ha, ___
Fmaj7 C Am Fmaj7 C
Ha, ___ ha, ___ ah, ___ ha. ___

A Pair Of Brown Eyes

Words & Music by Shane MacGowan

C G Am D

Intro | C | C ||

Verse 1

```
     G
One summer evening drunk to hell,
  Am              C
I sat there nearly lifeless.
   G
An old man in the corner sang
          C          Am
Where the water lilies grow.
    G
And on the jukebox Johnny sang
    Am                 C
A - bout a thing called love.
        G          Am     C        G
And it's how are you kid and what's your name,
    C                    Am
And how would you bloody know?
  G
In blood and death 'neath a screaming sky
  Am            C
I lay down on the ground,
        G
And the arms and legs of other men
    C           Am
Were scattered all a - round.
```

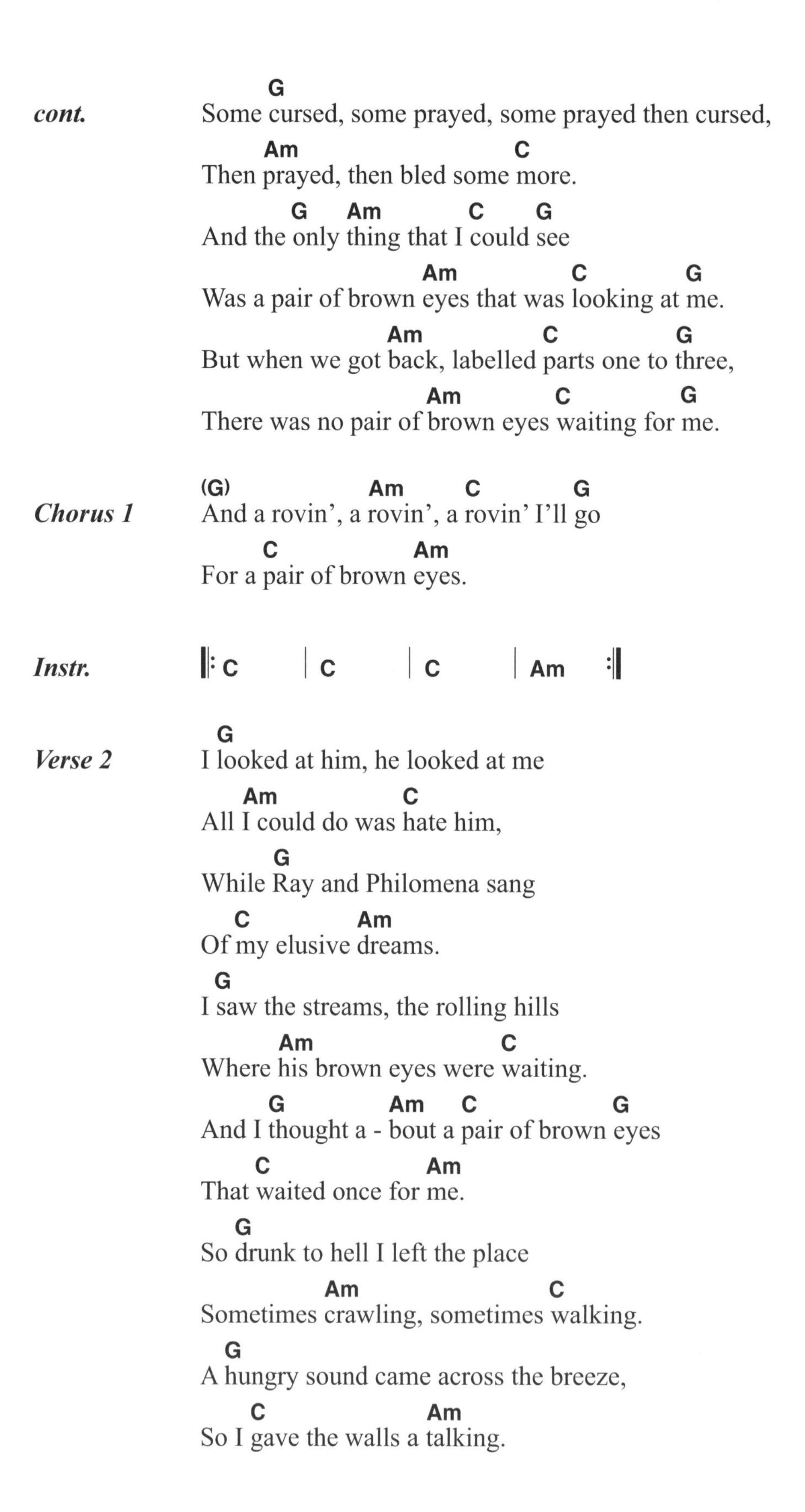

cont.

G
Some cursed, some prayed, some prayed then cursed,
Am C
Then prayed, then bled some more.
G Am C G
And the only thing that I could see
Am C G
Was a pair of brown eyes that was looking at me.
Am C G
But when we got back, labelled parts one to three,
Am C G
There was no pair of brown eyes waiting for me.

Chorus 1

(G) Am C G
And a rovin', a rovin', a rovin' I'll go
C Am
For a pair of brown eyes.

Instr.

‖: C | C | C | Am :‖

Verse 2

G
I looked at him, he looked at me
Am C
All I could do was hate him,
G
While Ray and Philomena sang
C Am
Of my elusive dreams.
G
I saw the streams, the rolling hills
Am C
Where his brown eyes were waiting.
G Am C G
And I thought a - bout a pair of brown eyes
C Am
That waited once for me.
G
So drunk to hell I left the place
Am C
Sometimes crawling, sometimes walking.
G
A hungry sound came across the breeze,
C Am
So I gave the walls a talking.

```
                G
cont.      And I heard the sounds of long ago
           Am                    C
           From the old ca - nal,
                  G           Am         C       G
           And the birds were whistling in the trees
                     C                   Am
           Where the wind was gently laughing.

                G         Am       C          G
Chorus 2   And a rovin', a rovin', a rovin' I'll go,
                      Am       C          G
           A rovin', a rovin', a rovin' I'll go,
                          Am       C          G
           And a rovin', a rovin', a rovin' I'll go
                C            Am
           For a pair of brown eyes,
                C       D      G
           For a pair of brown eyes.

           G              Am       C          G
Chorus 3   And a rovin', a rovin', a rovin' I'll go,
                          Am       C          G
           And a rovin', a rovin', a rovin' I'll go,
                          Am       C          G
           And a rovin', a rovin', a rovin' I'll go
                C            Am
           For a pair of brown eyes,
                C       D      G
           For a pair of brown eyes.    To fade
```

Parisienne Walkways

Words & Music by Gary Moore & Phil Lynott

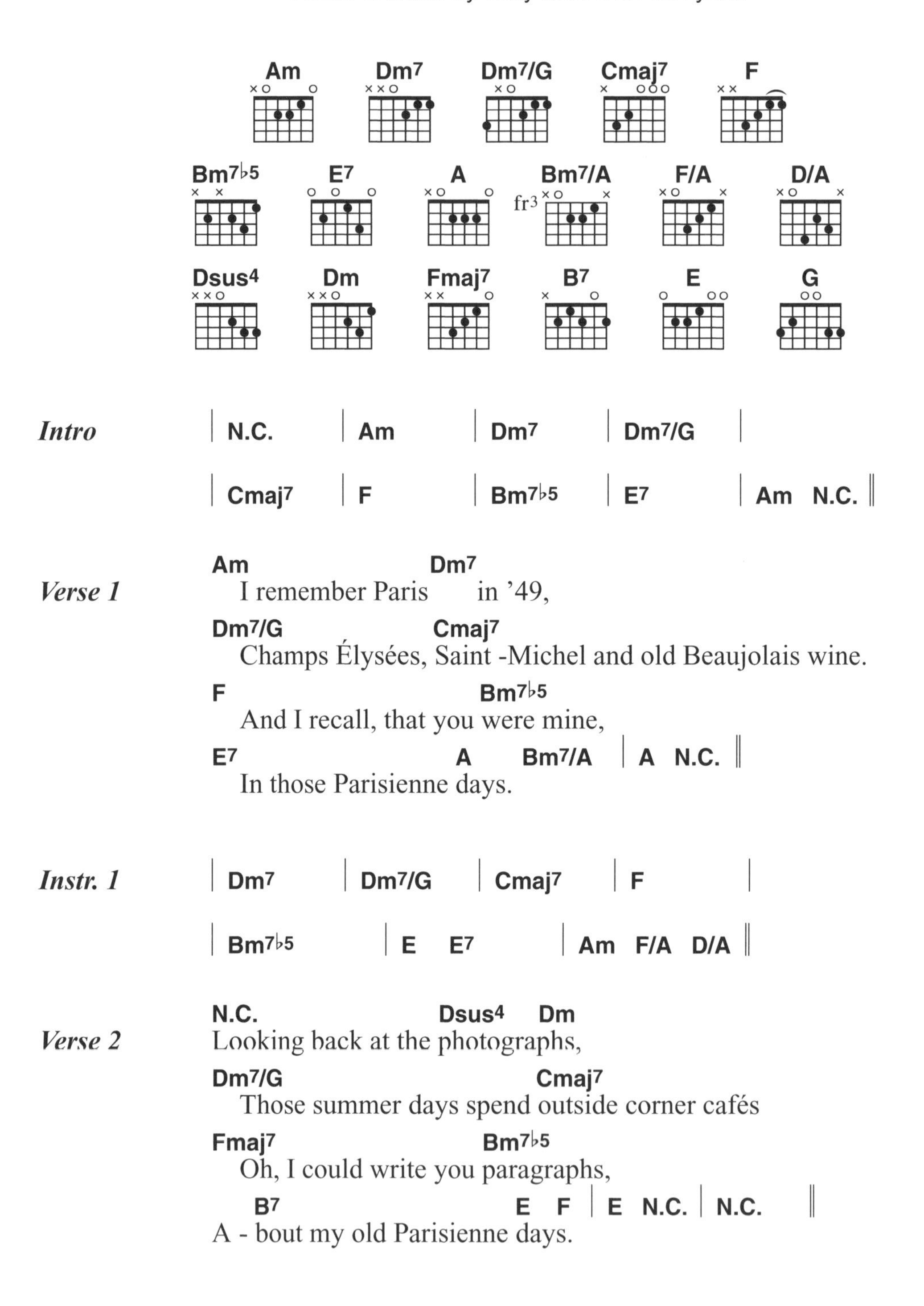

Instr. 2

Dm	Dm7/G	Cmaj7	Fmaj7
Bm7♭5 E	Am Dm	Am F E	Am Dm
Am F E	Am Dm	Am F E	Am Dm
Am F E	Am Dm	Am ‖ *To fade*

Rat Trap

Words & Music by Bob Geldof

G Em D/E C D

Am Bm G* Gsus4 Em* Esus4

Intro

| G | G | G | G | G | G |

| G | Em | G | Em |

| G | Em | G | Em | D/E ||

| G | Em | G | Em ||
(There was a)

Verse 1

```
               G                                  Em
There was a lot of rocking going on that night,
G                    Em
   Cruising time for the young bright lights,
G                                              Em
   Just down past the gasworks, by the meat factory door,
     C
The five lamp boys were coming on strong.
     G                                Em
The Saturday night city beat had already started and the,
G                                 Em
   The pulse of the corner boys just sprang into action,
  G                                Em
And young Billy watched under the yellow street light,
       C              D            Em
And said "Tonight of all nights    there's gonna be a fight".
```

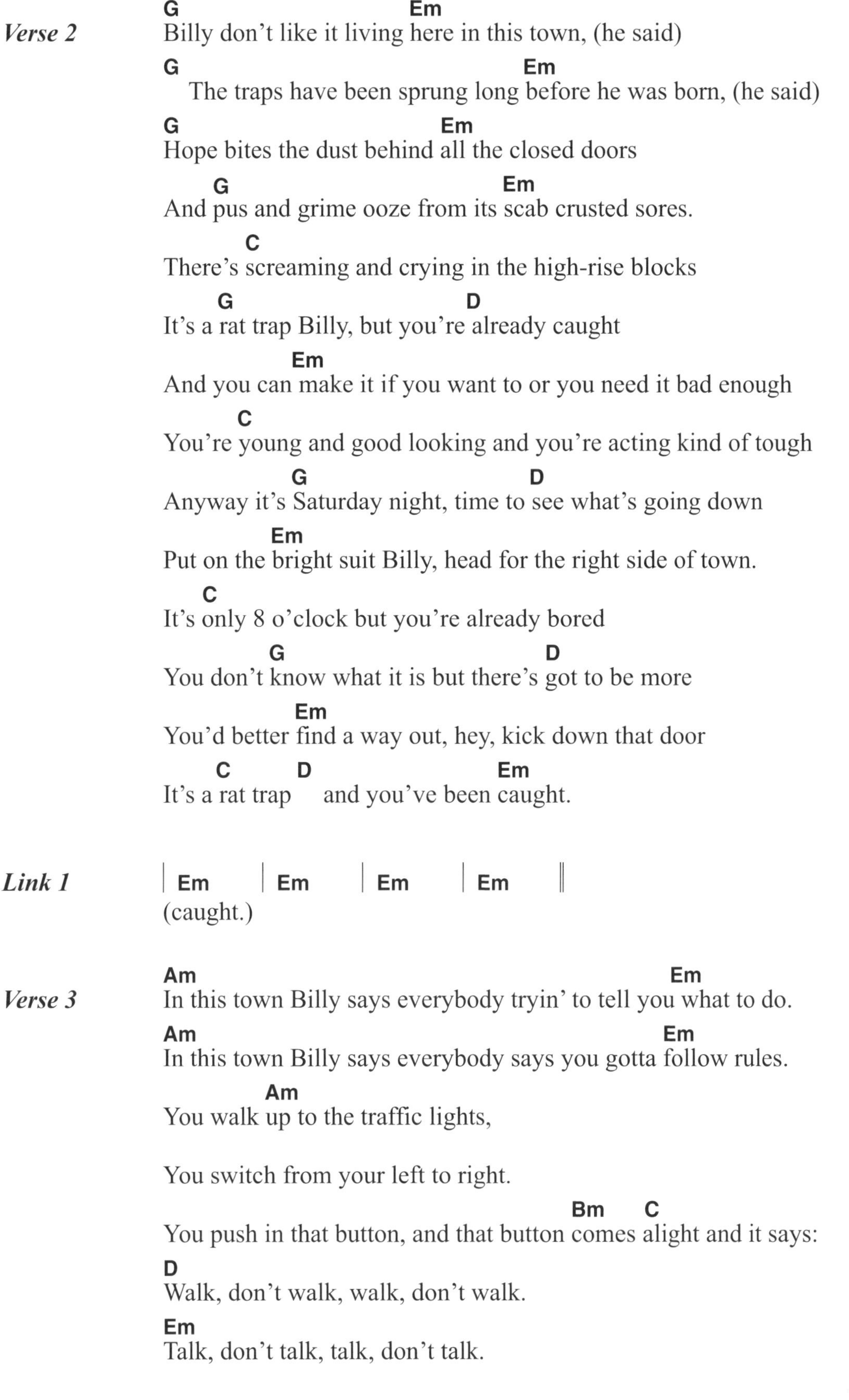

```
              G                                Em
Verse 2       Billy don't like it living here in this town, (he said)
              G                                           Em
                The traps have been sprung long before he was born, (he said)
              G                                Em
              Hope bites the dust behind all the closed doors
                  G                                 Em
              And pus and grime ooze from its scab crusted sores.
                    C
              There's screaming and crying in the high-rise blocks
                  G                           D
              It's a rat trap Billy, but you're already caught
                        Em
              And you can make it if you want to or you need it bad enough
                   C
              You're young and good looking and you're acting kind of tough
                         G                           D
              Anyway it's Saturday night, time to see what's going down
                       Em
              Put on the bright suit Billy, head for the right side of town.
                 C
              It's only 8 o'clock but you're already bored
                       G                             D
              You don't know what it is but there's got to be more
                         Em
              You'd better find a way out, hey, kick down that door
                  C      D                  Em
              It's a rat trap    and you've been caught.


Link 1        | Em    | Em    | Em    | Em    ||
              (caught.)


              Am                                                   Em
Verse 3       In this town Billy says everybody tryin' to tell you what to do.
              Am                                                  Em
              In this town Billy says everybody says you gotta follow rules.
                      Am
              You walk up to the traffic lights,

              You switch from your left to right.
                                                            Bm    C
              You push in that button, and that button comes alight and it says:
              D
              Walk, don't walk, walk, don't walk.
              Em
              Talk, don't talk, talk, don't talk.
```

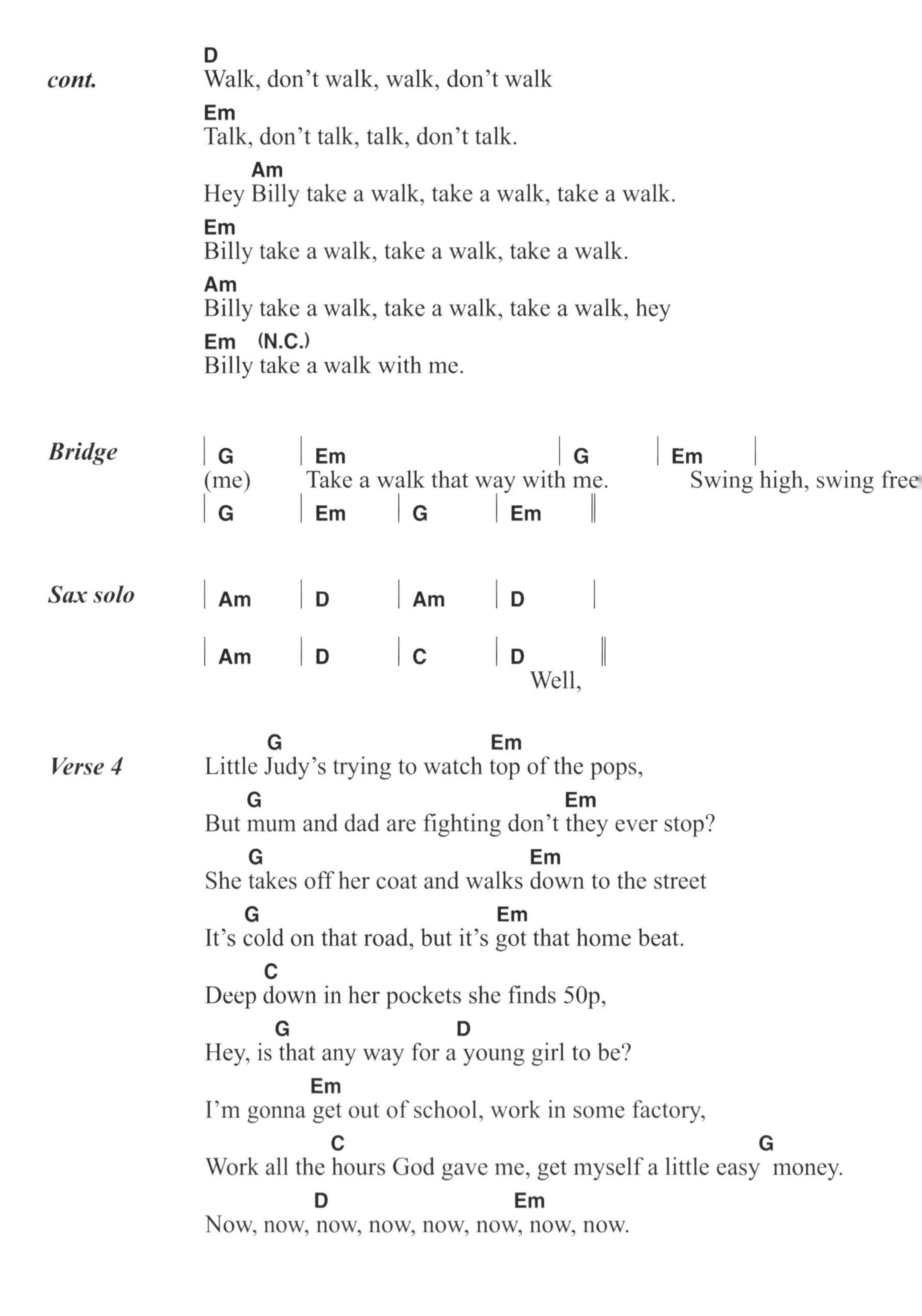

cont.

D
Walk, don't walk, walk, don't walk
Em
Talk, don't talk, talk, don't talk.
Am
Hey Billy take a walk, take a walk, take a walk.
Em
Billy take a walk, take a walk, take a walk.
Am
Billy take a walk, take a walk, take a walk, hey
Em (N.C.)
Billy take a walk with me.

Bridge

| G | Em | G | Em |
(me) Take a walk that way with me. Swing high, swing free
| G | Em | G | Em ||

Sax solo

| Am | D | Am | D |

| Am | D | C | D ||
Well,

Verse 4

G Em
Little Judy's trying to watch top of the pops,
G Em
But mum and dad are fighting don't they ever stop?
G Em
She takes off her coat and walks down to the street
G Em
It's cold on that road, but it's got that home beat.
C
Deep down in her pockets she finds 50p,
G D
Hey, is that any way for a young girl to be?
Em
I'm gonna get out of school, work in some factory,
C G
Work all the hours God gave me, get myself a little easy money.
D Em
Now, now, now, now, now, now, now, now.

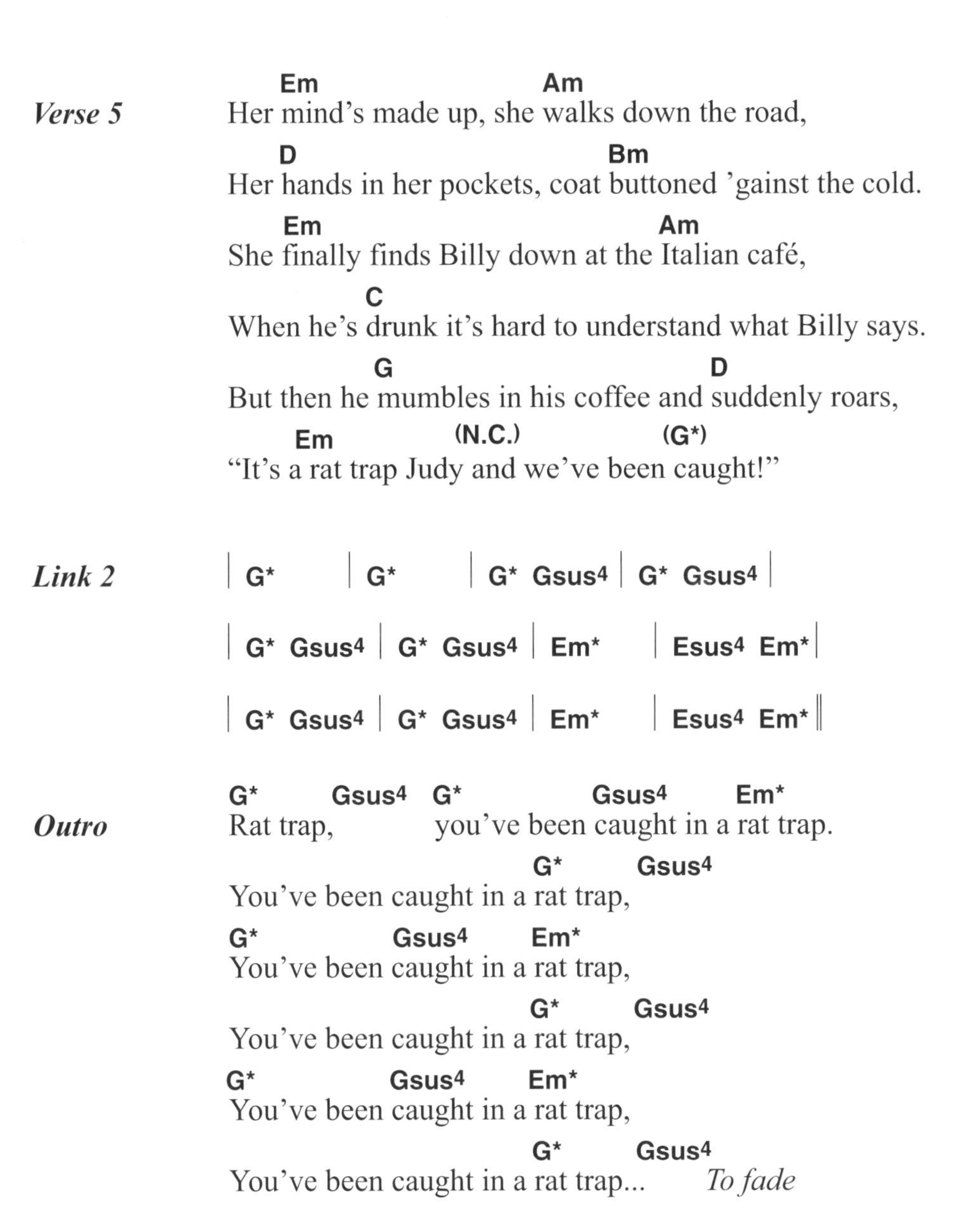

Verse 5

```
      Em                      Am
Her mind's made up, she walks down the road,
     D                              Bm
Her hands in her pockets, coat buttoned 'gainst the cold.
      Em                                  Am
She finally finds Billy down at the Italian café,
              C
When he's drunk it's hard to understand what Billy says.
               G                             D
But then he mumbles in his coffee and suddenly roars,
       Em            (N.C.)               (G*)
"It's a rat trap Judy and we've been caught!"
```

Link 2

G*	G*	G* Gsus4	G* Gsus4
G* Gsus4	G* Gsus4	Em*	Esus4 Em*
G* Gsus4	G* Gsus4	Em*	Esus4 Em*	

Outro

```
G*       Gsus4  G*          Gsus4      Em*
Rat trap,       you've been caught in a rat trap.
                          G*      Gsus4
You've been caught in a rat trap,
G*           Gsus4       Em*
You've been caught in a rat trap,
                          G*      Gsus4
You've been caught in a rat trap,
G*           Gsus4       Em*
You've been caught in a rat trap,
                          G*      Gsus4
You've been caught in a rat trap...       To fade
```

Ride On

Words & Music by Jimmy MacCarthy

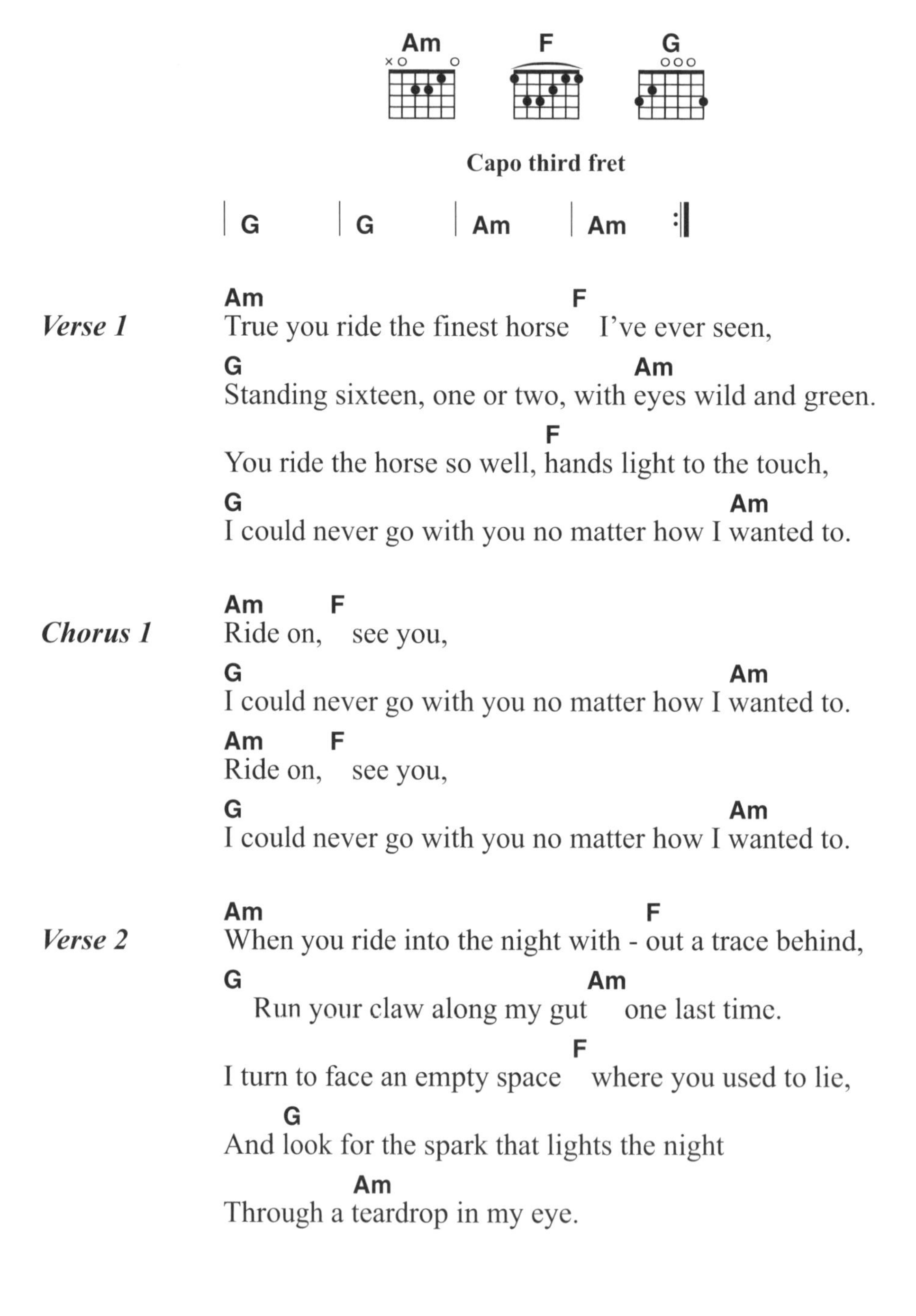

Capo third fret

| G | G | Am | Am :|

Verse 1

```
Am                             F
True you ride the finest horse    I've ever seen,
G                                         Am
Standing sixteen, one or two, with eyes wild and green.
                                F
You ride the horse so well, hands light to the touch,
G                                                  Am
I could never go with you no matter how I wanted to.
```

Chorus 1

```
Am        F
Ride on,     see you,
G                                                  Am
I could never go with you no matter how I wanted to.
Am        F
Ride on,     see you,
G                                                  Am
I could never go with you no matter how I wanted to.
```

Verse 2

```
Am                                       F
When you ride into the night with - out a trace behind,
G                                   Am
   Run your claw along my gut     one last time.
                                   F
I turn to face an empty space    where you used to lie,
     G
And look for the spark that lights the night
               Am
Through a teardrop in my eye.
```

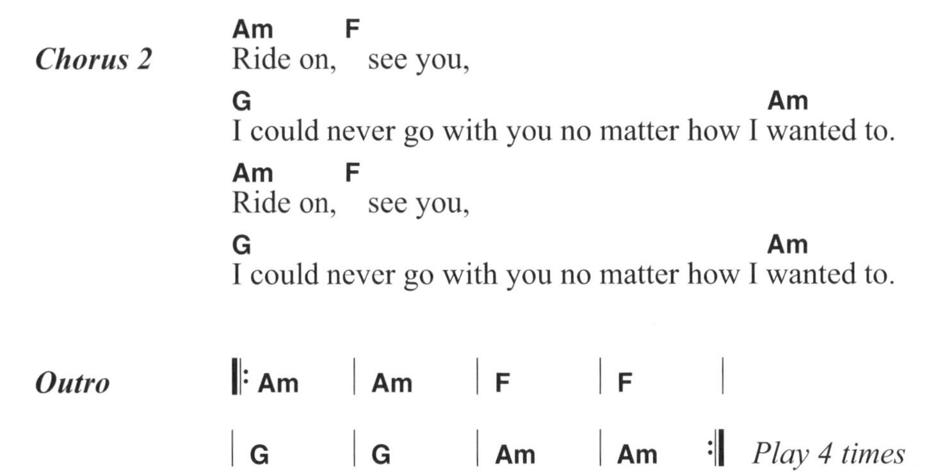

Chorus 2

Am F
Ride on, see you,
G Am
I could never go with you no matter how I wanted to.
Am F
Ride on, see you,
G Am
I could never go with you no matter how I wanted to.

Outro

|: Am | Am | F | F |
| G | G | Am | Am :| *Play 4 times*

Run

Words & Music by Gary Lightbody, Jonathan Quinn, Mark McClelland, Nathan Connolly & Iain Archer

Am F/A G5 Gsus4 C G F

Intro ‖: Am F/A | G5 Gsus4 G5 | Am F/A | G5 Gsus4 G5 :‖

Verse 1

```
                Am          F/A  G5    Gsus4  G5
I'll sing it one last time for    you
             Am          F/A    G5    Gsus4   G5
Then we really have to     go
                    Am          F/A        G5  Gsus4   G5
You've been the only thing that's right
           Am       F/A   G5      Gsus4   G5
In all I've     done.
```

Verse 2

```
               Am           F/A     G5     Gsus4   G5
And I can barely look at you
               Am         F/A    G5     Gsus4   G5
But every single time I     do
                  Am          F/A         G5  Gsus4    G5
I know we'll make it an - y - where
                 Am       F/A   G5     Gsus4   G5
Away from       here.
```

Chorus 1

```
C
  Light up, light up
          G
As if you have a choice
                            Am
Even if you cannot hear my voice
                             F    | F      |
I'll be right beside you dear
C
 Louder, louder
              G
And we'll run for our lives
                             Am
I can hardly speak I understand
                                       F    | F      |
Why you can't raise your voice to say.
```

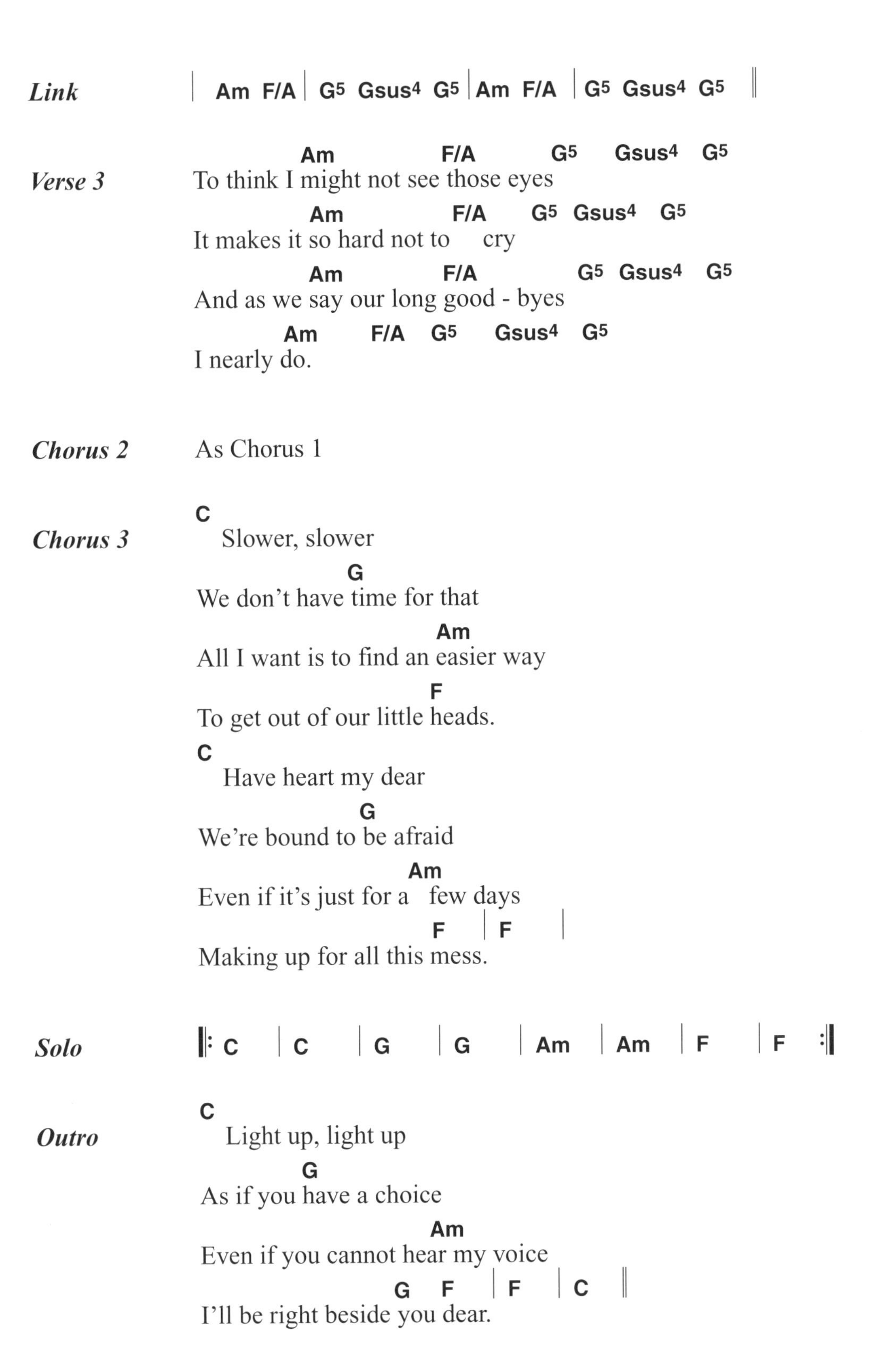

Link | Am F/A | G5 Gsus4 G5 | Am F/A | G5 Gsus4 G5 ||

Verse 3

Am F/A G5 Gsus4 G5
To think I might not see those eyes
Am F/A G5 Gsus4 G5
It makes it so hard not to cry
Am F/A G5 Gsus4 G5
And as we say our long good - byes
Am F/A G5 Gsus4 G5
I nearly do.

Chorus 2 As Chorus 1

Chorus 3

C
Slower, slower
G
We don't have time for that
Am
All I want is to find an easier way
F
To get out of our little heads.
C
Have heart my dear
G
We're bound to be afraid
Am
Even if it's just for a few days
F | F |
Making up for all this mess.

Solo ||: C | C | G | G | Am | Am | F | F :||

Outro

C
Light up, light up
G
As if you have a choice
Am
Even if you cannot hear my voice
G F | F | C ||
I'll be right beside you dear.

Runaway

Words & Music by Andrea Corr, Caroline Corr, Sharon Corr & Jim Corr

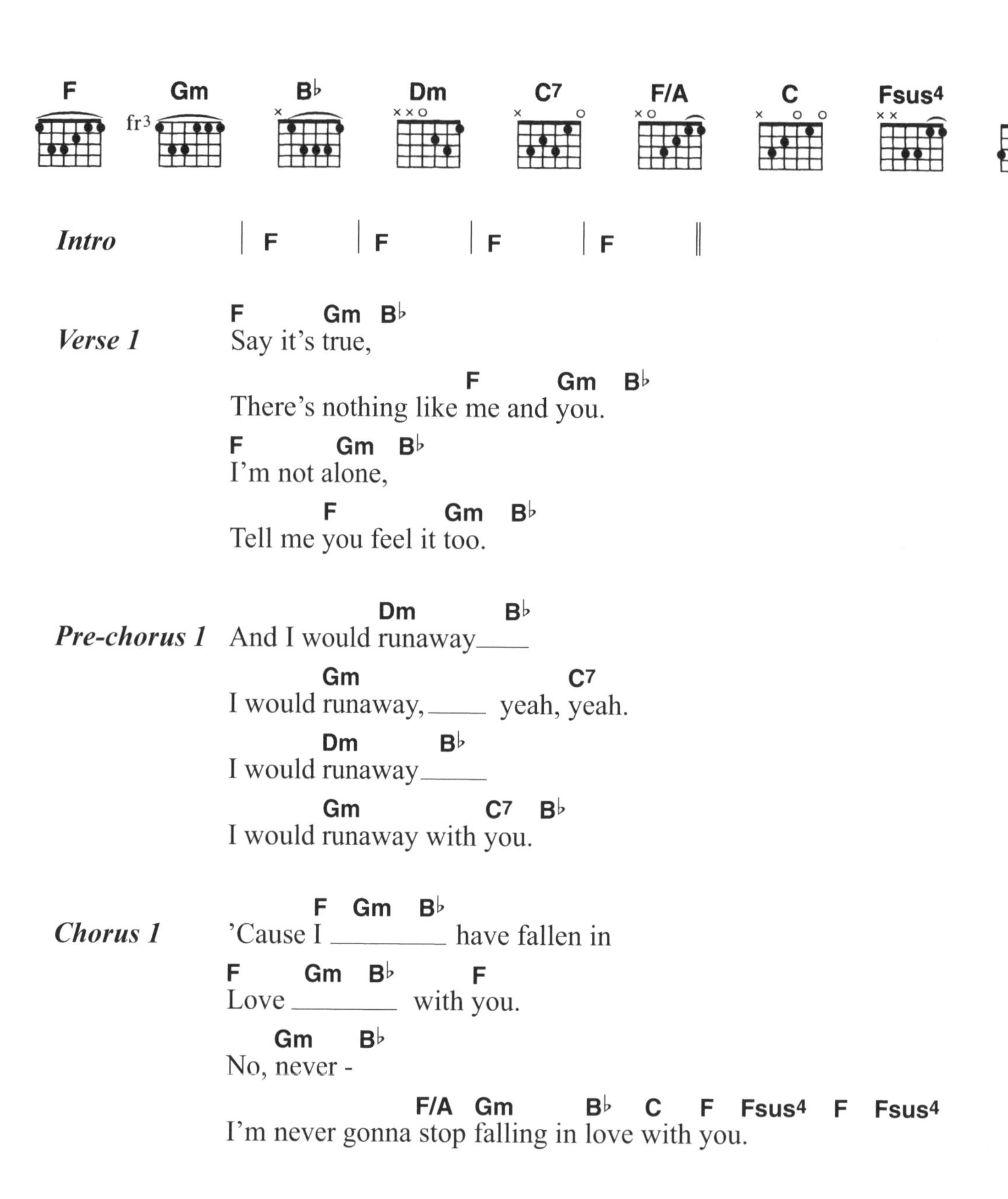

Intro | F | F | F | F ||

Verse 1

```
F          Gm  B♭
Say it's true,
                     F          Gm    B♭
There's nothing like me and you.
F            Gm   B♭
I'm not alone,
           F              Gm    B♭
Tell me you feel it too.
```

Pre-chorus 1

```
                   Dm          B♭
And I would runaway____
           Gm                   C7
I would runaway,____ yeah, yeah.
           Dm          B♭
I would runaway____
           Gm               C7   B♭
I would runaway with you.
```

Chorus 1

```
            F   Gm   B♭
'Cause I ________ have fallen in
F      Gm   B♭       F
Love ________ with you.
        Gm      B♭
No, never -
                          F/A  Gm         B♭    C    F   Fsus4   F   Fsus4
I'm never gonna stop falling in love with you.
```

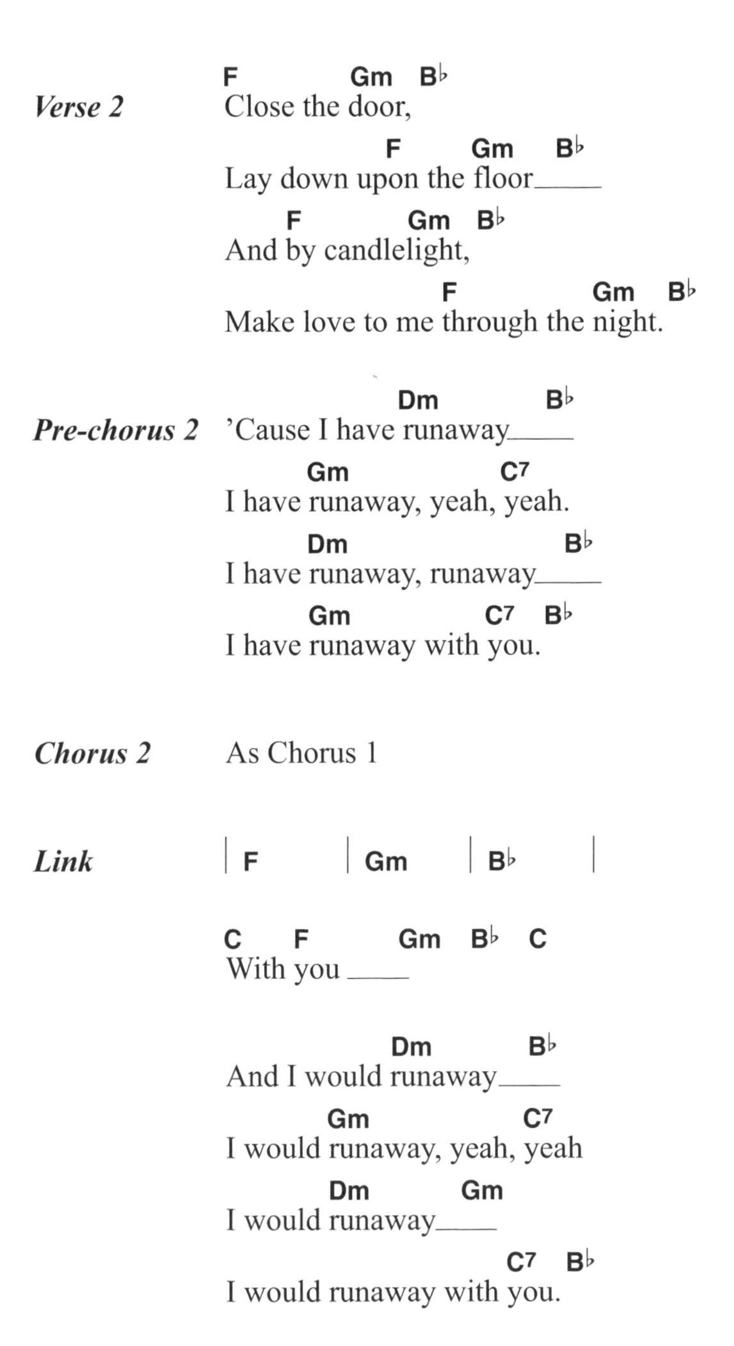

Verse 2

F Gm B♭
Close the door,

F Gm B♭
Lay down upon the floor___

F Gm B♭
And by candlelight,

F Gm B♭
Make love to me through the night.

Pre-chorus 2

Dm B♭
'Cause I have runaway___

Gm C7
I have runaway, yeah, yeah.

Dm B♭
I have runaway, runaway___

Gm C7 B♭
I have runaway with you.

Chorus 2 As Chorus 1

Link | F | Gm | B♭ |

C F Gm B♭ C
With you ___

Dm B♭
And I would runaway___

Gm C7
I would runaway, yeah, yeah

Dm Gm
I would runaway___

C7 B♭
I would runaway with you.

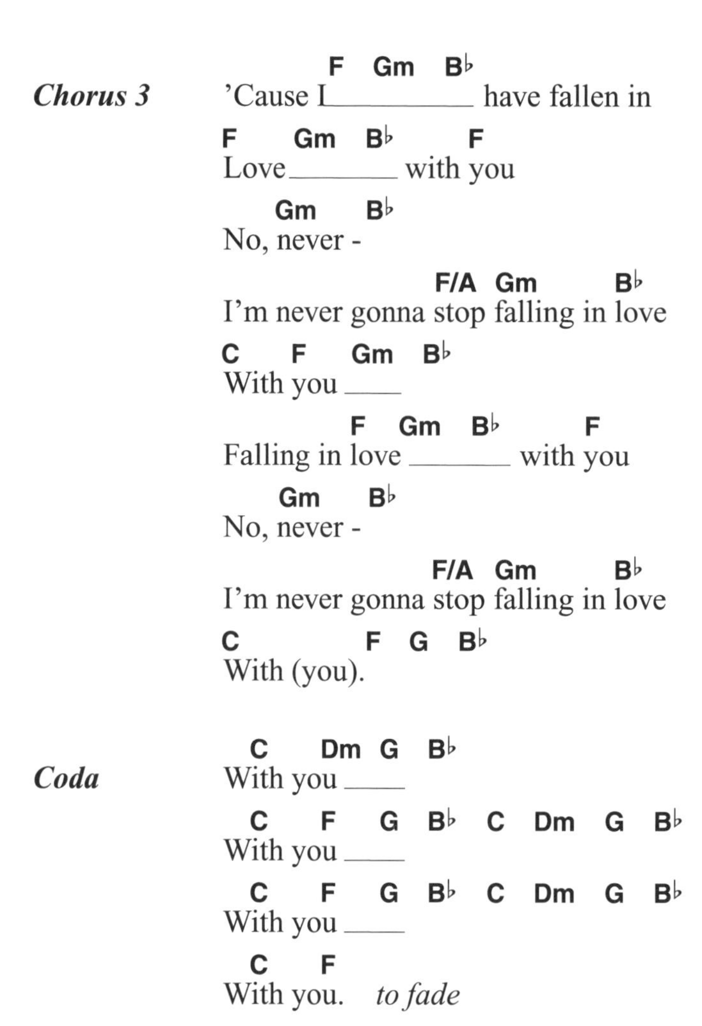

Chorus 3

F Gm B♭
'Cause I ________ have fallen in

F Gm B♭ F
Love ______ with you

Gm B♭
No, never -

F/A Gm B♭
I'm never gonna stop falling in love

C F Gm B♭
With you ___

F Gm B♭ F
Falling in love ______ with you

Gm B♭
No, never -

F/A Gm B♭
I'm never gonna stop falling in love

C F G B♭
With (you).

Coda

C Dm G B♭
With you ___

C F G B♭ C Dm G B♭
With you ___

C F G B♭ C Dm G B♭
With you ___

C F
With you. *to fade*

Seven Drunken Nights

Traditional
Arranged by Ronnie Drew, Ciaran Bourke, Luke Kelly, Barney McKenna & John Sheahan

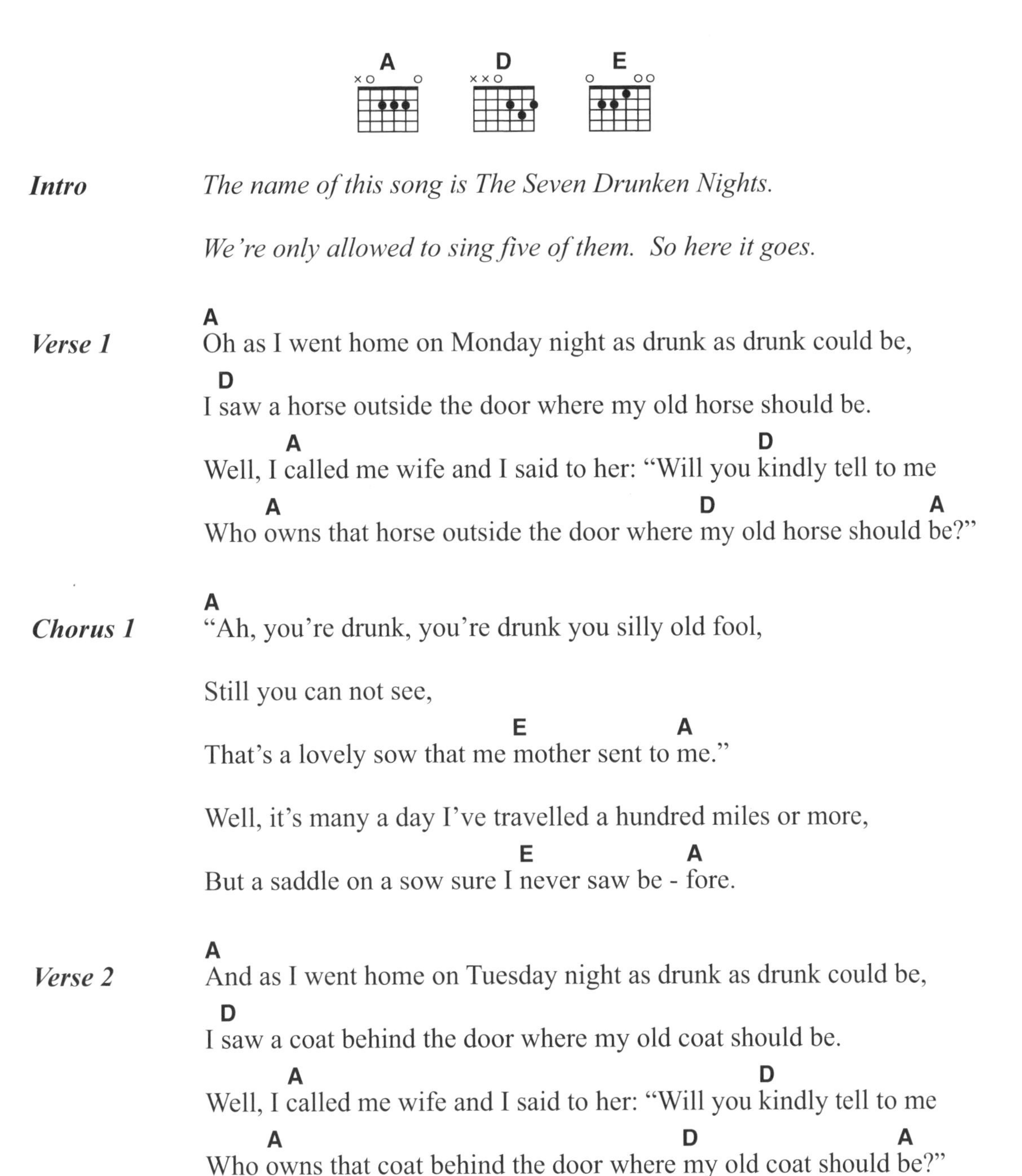

Intro

The name of this song is The Seven Drunken Nights.

We're only allowed to sing five of them. So here it goes.

Verse 1

A
Oh as I went home on Monday night as drunk as drunk could be,
D
I saw a horse outside the door where my old horse should be.
A D
Well, I called me wife and I said to her: "Will you kindly tell to me
A D A
Who owns that horse outside the door where my old horse should be?"

Chorus 1

A
"Ah, you're drunk, you're drunk you silly old fool,

Still you can not see,
E A
That's a lovely sow that me mother sent to me."

Well, it's many a day I've travelled a hundred miles or more,
E A
But a saddle on a sow sure I never saw be - fore.

Verse 2

A
And as I went home on Tuesday night as drunk as drunk could be,
D
I saw a coat behind the door where my old coat should be.
A D
Well, I called me wife and I said to her: "Will you kindly tell to me
A D A
Who owns that coat behind the door where my old coat should be?"

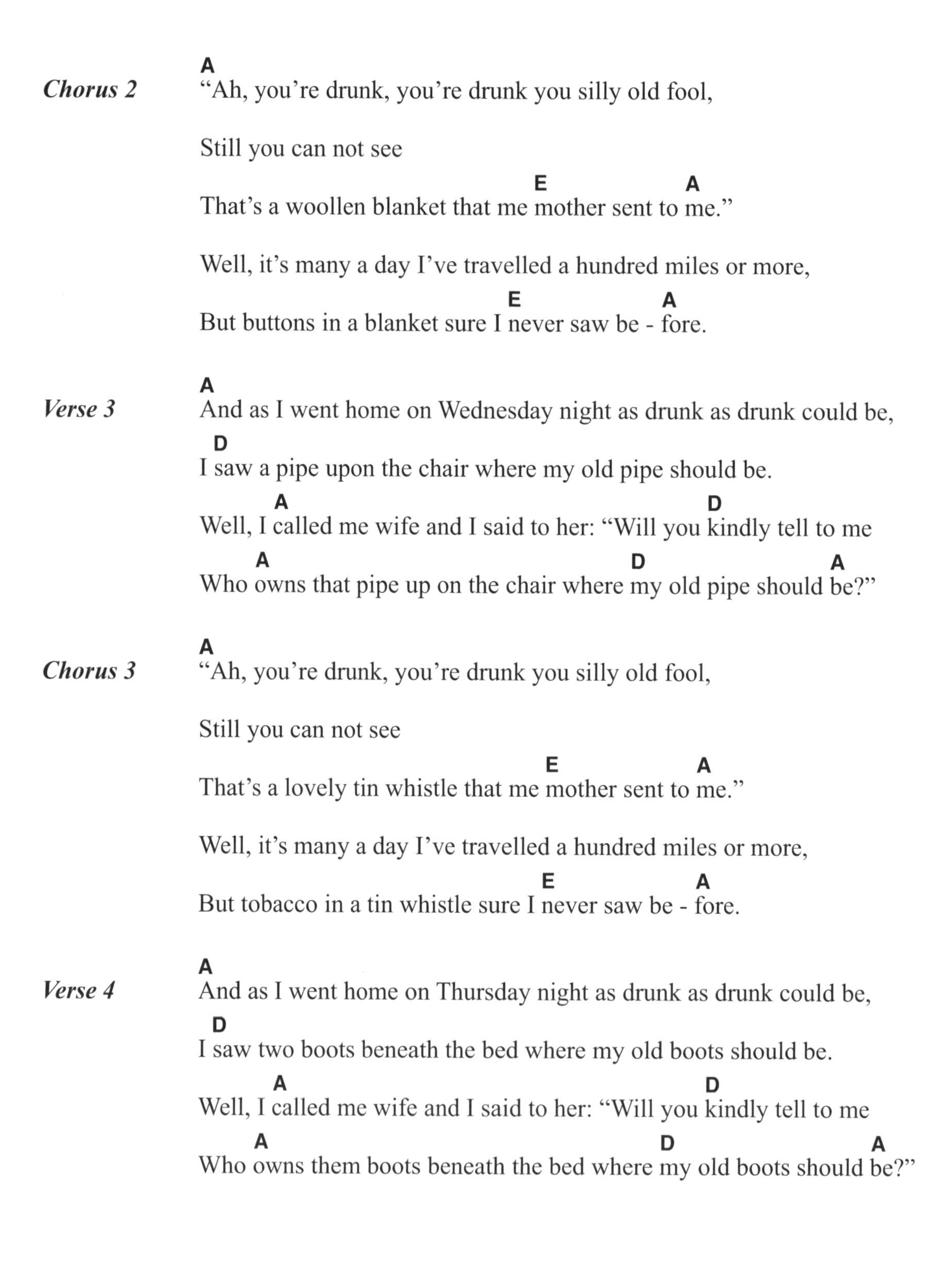

Chorus 2

A
"Ah, you're drunk, you're drunk you silly old fool,

Still you can not see

E A
That's a woollen blanket that me mother sent to me."

Well, it's many a day I've travelled a hundred miles or more,

E A
But buttons in a blanket sure I never saw be - fore.

Verse 3

A
And as I went home on Wednesday night as drunk as drunk could be,

D
I saw a pipe upon the chair where my old pipe should be.

A D
Well, I called me wife and I said to her: "Will you kindly tell to me

A D A
Who owns that pipe up on the chair where my old pipe should be?"

Chorus 3

A
"Ah, you're drunk, you're drunk you silly old fool,

Still you can not see

E A
That's a lovely tin whistle that me mother sent to me."

Well, it's many a day I've travelled a hundred miles or more,

E A
But tobacco in a tin whistle sure I never saw be - fore.

Verse 4

A
And as I went home on Thursday night as drunk as drunk could be,

D
I saw two boots beneath the bed where my old boots should be.

A D
Well, I called me wife and I said to her: "Will you kindly tell to me

A D A
Who owns them boots beneath the bed where my old boots should be?"

Chorus 4

A
"Ah, you're drunk, you're drunk you silly old fool,

Still you can not see

E A
They're two lovely geranium pots me mother sent to me."

Well, it's many a day I've travelled a hundred miles or more,

E A
But laces in geranium pots I never saw be - fore.

Verse 5

A
And as I went home on Friday night as drunk as drunk could be,

D
I saw a head upon the bed where my old head should be.

A D
Well, I called me wife and I said to her: "Will you kindly tell to me

A D A
Who owns that head upon the bed where my old head should be?"

Chorus 5

A
"Ah, you're drunk, you're drunk you silly old fool,

Still you can not see

E A
That's a baby boy that me mother sent to me."

Well, it's many a day I've travelled a hundred miles or more,

E A E A
But a baby boy with his whiskers on sure I never saw be - fore.

Saints & Sinners

Words & Music by Patrick Maher

A7 D Bm Gmaj7 A7/E D5/G

Capo fourth fret

Verse 1

```
A7                          D
   Well anyone can lose it all,
                    Bm
Well anyone can lose it all.
                                       D
   When you don't heed your warning's call,
     A7
Well anyone can lose it all.
                          D
Well anyone can make a mess,
                      Bm
Yeah, anyone can make a mess.
Gmaj7                            D
   Just take so much and make it less,
     A7
Well anyone can make a mess.
```

Chorus 1

```
(A7)          D                                A7/E
When you got time and streets making saints and sinners,
                                   Gmaj7
Well ink on sheets makin' losers the winners.
                        D              A7
Well it's not what your dreams should be.
```

Verse 2

```
N.C.                     D
Well anyone can be a saint,
                      Bm
Well anyone can be       a saint.
Gmaj7                             D
   When you just forget that you ain't,
      A7
We can go and be a saint.
```

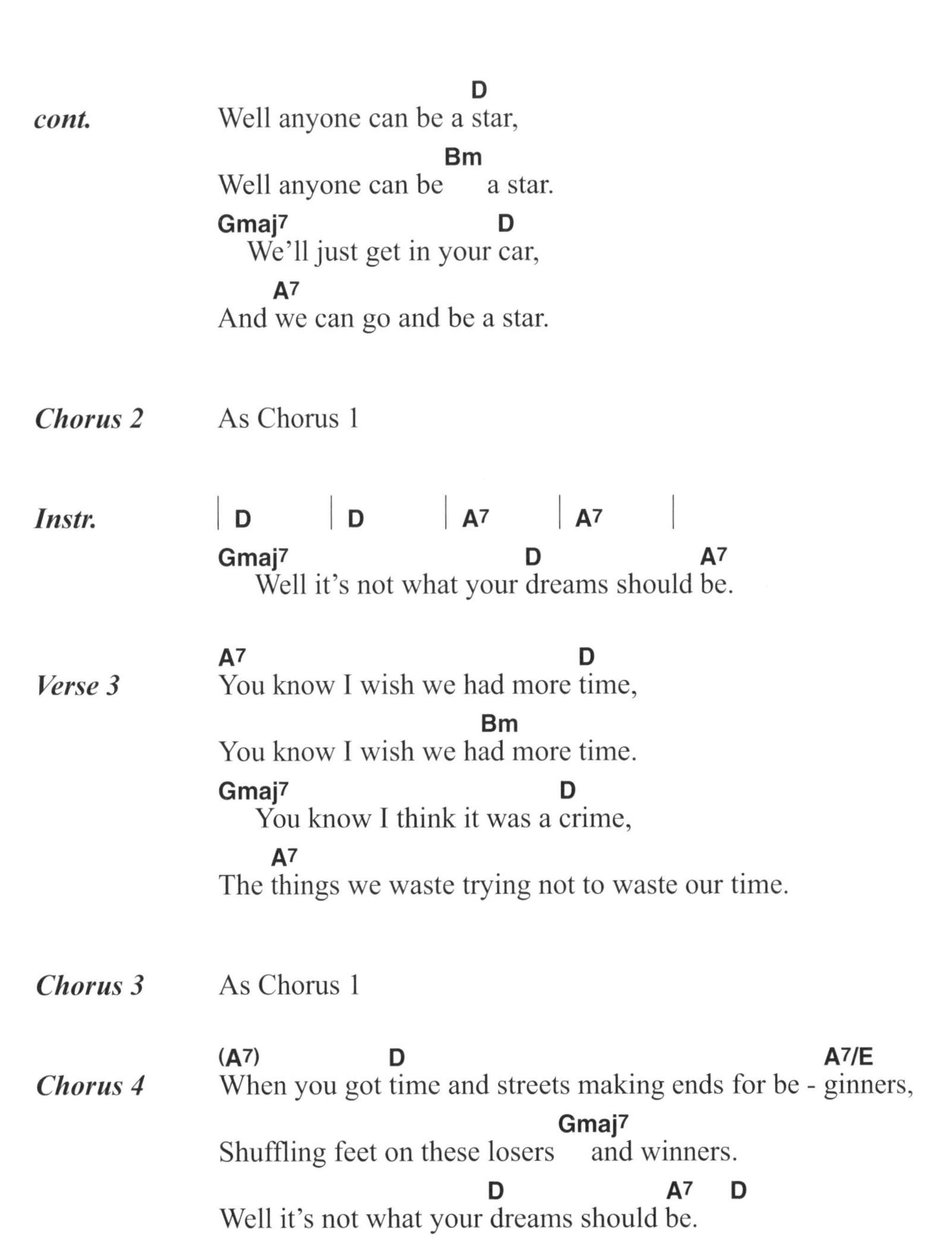

cont.

D
Well anyone can be a star,
Bm
Well anyone can be a star.
Gmaj7 D
We'll just get in your car,
A7
And we can go and be a star.

Chorus 2 As Chorus 1

Instr. | D | D | A7 | A7 |

Gmaj7 D A7
Well it's not what your dreams should be.

Verse 3

A7 D
You know I wish we had more time,
Bm
You know I wish we had more time.
Gmaj7 D
You know I think it was a crime,
A7
The things we waste trying not to waste our time.

Chorus 3 As Chorus 1

Chorus 4

(A7) D A7/E
When you got time and streets making ends for be - ginners,
Gmaj7
Shuffling feet on these losers and winners.
D A7 D
Well it's not what your dreams should be.

Say It To Me Now

Words & Music by Glen Hansard, Paul Brennan, David Odlum, Graham Downey & Noreen O'Donnell

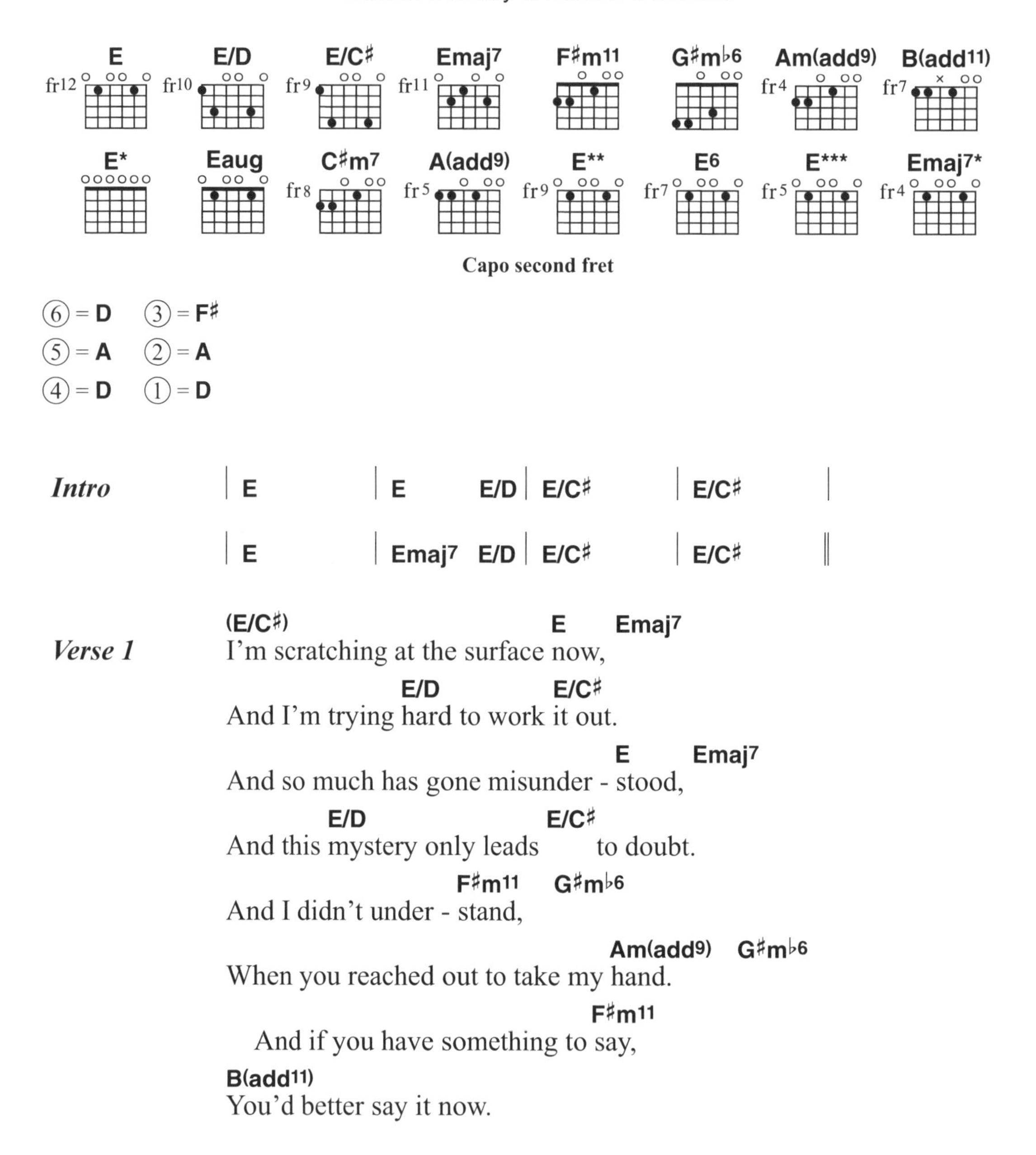

Capo second fret

⑥ = D ③ = F♯
⑤ = A ② = A
④ = D ① = D

Intro | E | E E/D | E/C♯ | E/C♯ |

| E | Emaj7 E/D | E/C♯ | E/C♯ ||

Verse 1

(E/C♯) E Emaj7
I'm scratching at the surface now,
E/D E/C♯
And I'm trying hard to work it out.
E Emaj7
And so much has gone misunder - stood,
E/D E/C♯
And this mystery only leads to doubt.
F♯m11 G♯m♭6
And I didn't under - stand,
Am(add9) G♯m♭6
When you reached out to take my hand.
F♯m11
And if you have something to say,
B(add11)
You'd better say it now.

Chorus 1

```
E*                                    Eaug
   'Cause this is what you've waited for,
C#m7                          A(add9)
   Your chance to even up the score.
E*                          Eaug       C#m7
   And as these shadows fall on me now,
              A(add9)
I will some - how. Yeah.
E*                                   Eaug
   'Cause I'm picking up a message Lord,
C#m7                                    A(add9)
   And I'm closer than I've ever been before.
E*                                B(add11)
   So if you have something to say,
             A(add9)
Say it to me now.
B(add11)            A(add9)
   Just say it to me now,
B(add11)   A(add9)      B(add11)     E**   E6   E***   Emaj7*   E***
   Oh,__________  oh,___         oh.__
```

Screamager

Words & Music by Andrew Cairns, Michael McKeegan & Fyfe Ewing

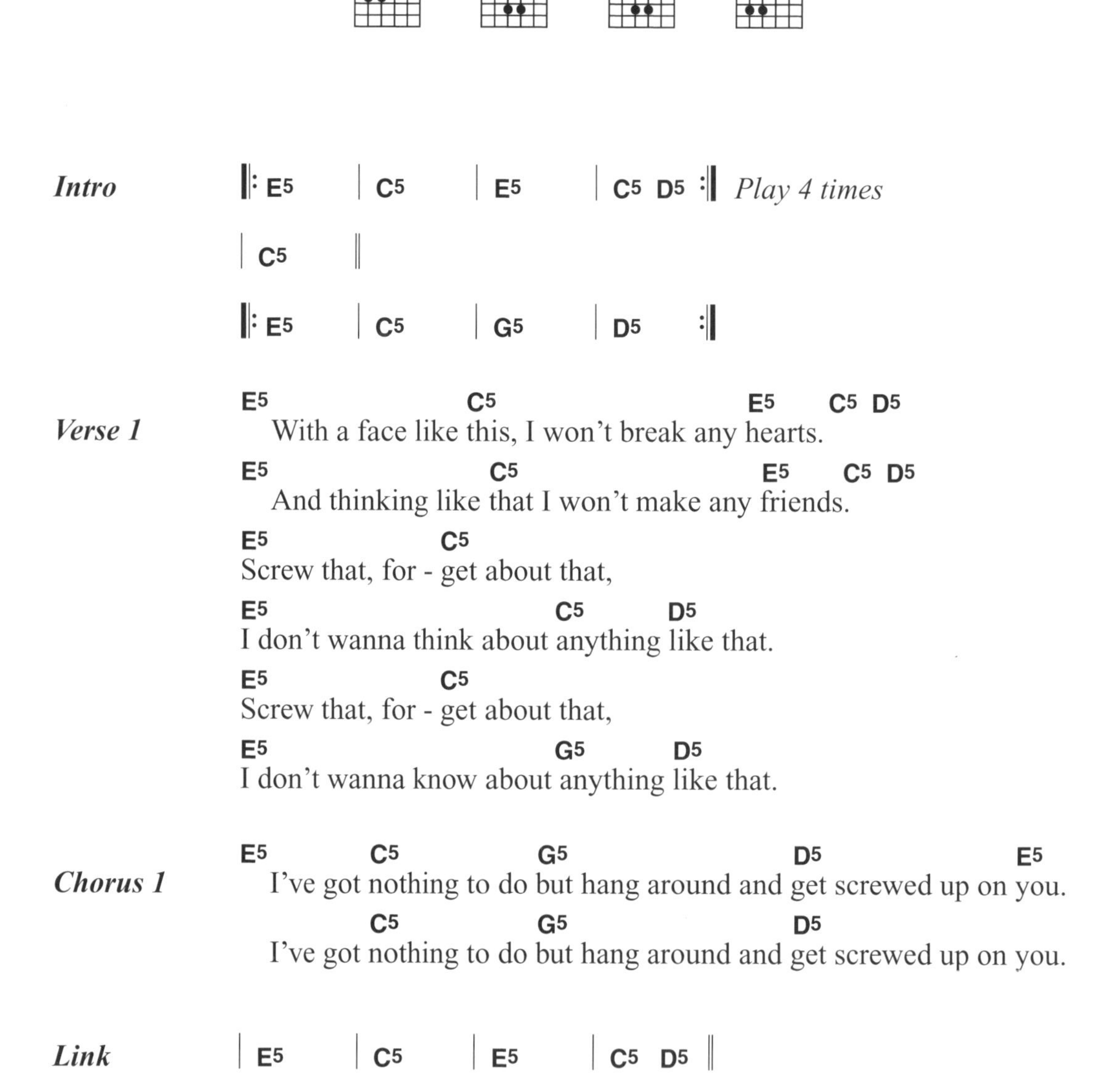

Intro

|: E5 | C5 | E5 | C5 D5 :| *Play 4 times*

| C5 ||

|: E5 | C5 | G5 | D5 :|

Verse 1

```
E5                C5                    E5    C5  D5
   With a face like this, I won't break any hearts.
E5                  C5                    E5    C5  D5
   And thinking like that I won't make any friends.
E5                C5
Screw that, for - get about that,
E5                          C5          D5
I don't wanna think about anything like that.
E5                C5
Screw that, for - get about that,
E5                          G5          D5
I don't wanna know about anything like that.
```

Chorus 1

```
E5         C5           G5                         D5                    E5
   I've got nothing to do but hang around and get screwed up on you.
           C5           G5                         D5
   I've got nothing to do but hang around and get screwed up on you.
```

Link

| E5 | C5 | E5 | C5 D5 ||

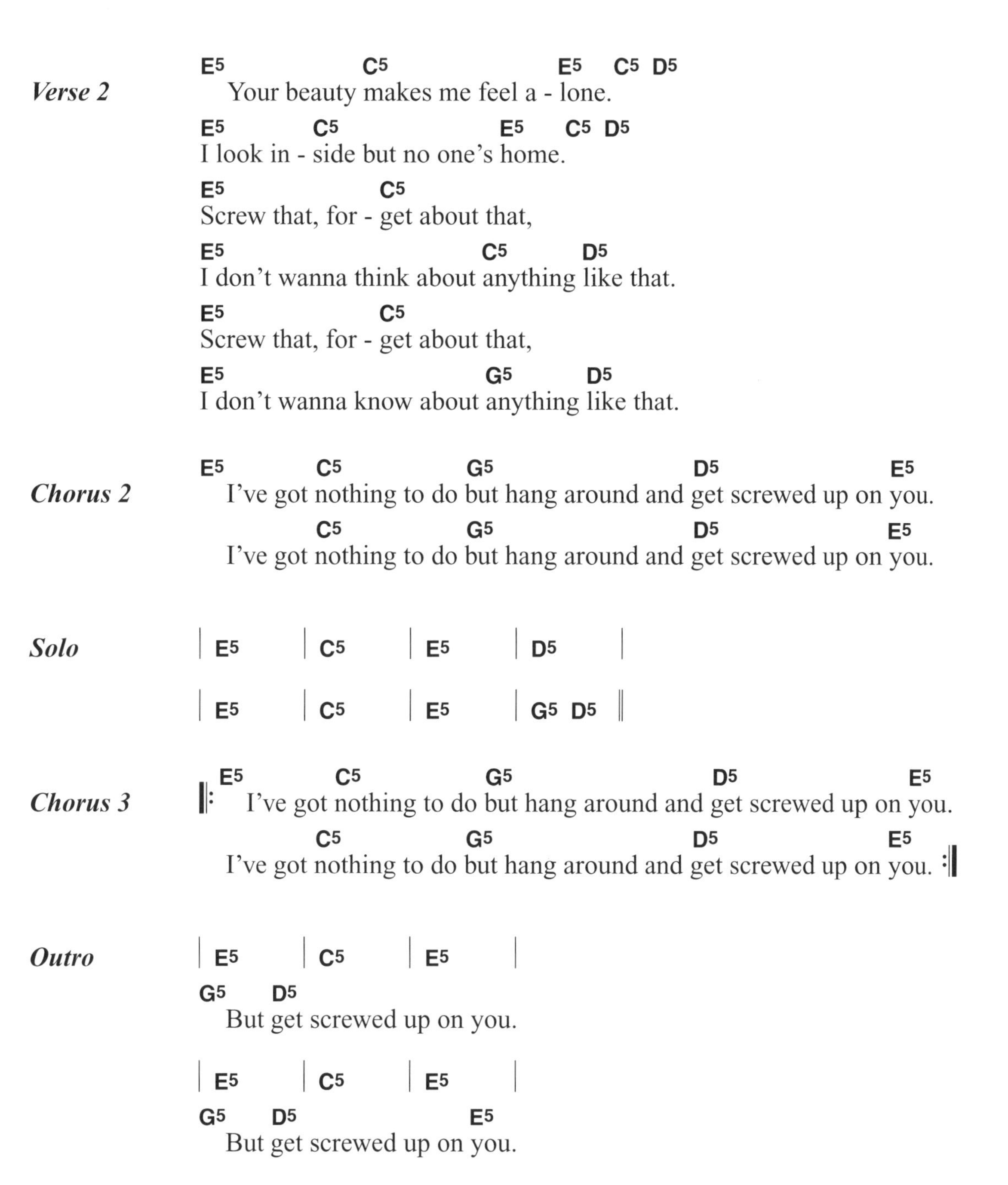
Verse 2
E5 C5 E5 C5 D5
Your beauty makes me feel a - lone.
E5 C5 E5 C5 D5
I look in - side but no one's home.
E5 C5
Screw that, for - get about that,
E5 C5 D5
I don't wanna think about anything like that.
E5 C5
Screw that, for - get about that,
E5 G5 D5
I don't wanna know about anything like that.
Chorus 2
E5 C5 G5 D5 E5
I've got nothing to do but hang around and get screwed up on you.
C5 G5 D5 E5
I've got nothing to do but hang around and get screwed up on you.
Solo
E5 C5 E5 D5
E5 C5 E5 G5 D5
Chorus 3
E5 C5 G5 D5 E5
I've got nothing to do but hang around and get screwed up on you.
C5 G5 D5 E5
I've got nothing to do but hang around and get screwed up on you.
Outro
E5 C5 E5
G5 D5
But get screwed up on you.
E5 C5 E5
G5 D5 E5
But get screwed up on you.

Songs Of Love

Words & Music by Neil Hannon

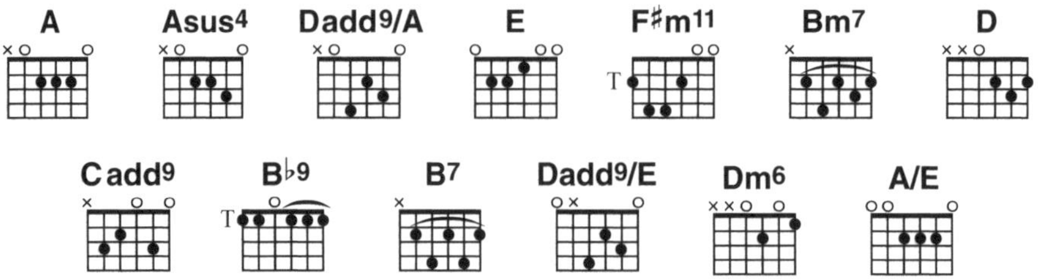

A Asus4 Dadd9/A E F♯m11 Bm7 D

Cadd9 B♭9 B7 Dadd9/E Dm6 A/E

Capo third fret

Intro | A Asus4 | A Asus4 | A Asus4 | A Asus4 ||

Verse 1

```
A                  Dadd9/A
Pale, pubescent beasts
                     E                  F♯m11
Roam through the streets and coffee-shops;
      Bm7          D
Their prey gather in herds
                      Cadd9                  B♭9
Of stiff knee-length skirts and white ankle-socks.
    A                       Dadd9/A
But while they search for a mate
                  E                  F♯m11
My type hibernate in bedrooms above
          B7        D      Dadd9/E
Composing their songs   of (love.)
```

Link | A | A ||
love.

Verse 2

```
A                 D
Young, uniform minds
               E                  F♯m11
In uniform lines and uniform ties
       Bm7                 D
Run round with trousers on fire
                Cadd9                 B♭9
And signs of desire they cannot disguise,
```

cont.

A D
While I try to find words,
E F♯m11
As light as the birds that circle above
B7 D Dadd9/E
To put in my songs of (love.)

Link 2

| A | A ||
love. ________

Bridge 1

F Dm6 A F♯m11
Fate doesn't hang on a wrong, or right choice,
F Dm6 A/E E
Fortune depends on the tone of your voice.

Chorus 1

A D
So sing while you have time,
E F♯m11
Let the sun shine down from above
B7 D Dadd9/E A
And fill you with songs of love.____ (Take me.)

Solo

A	D	E	F♯m11	Bm7	D
Cadd9	B♭9	A	D	E	F♯m11
B7	D Dadd9/E	A	A	

Bridge 2

As Bridge 1

Chorus 2

A D
So let's sing while we still can,
E F♯m11
While the sun hangs high up above
B7 D Dadd9/E F♯m11
Wonderful songs of love, _______
B7 D Dadd9/E A
Beautiful songs of (love.)

Coda

| A | A | A | A ||
love. _______

Sunday Bloody Sunday

Words & Music by U2

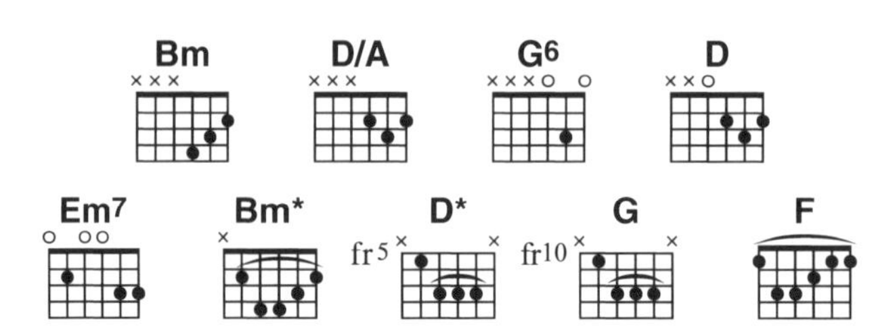

Tune guitar down a semitone

Intro | Bm D/A | G6 | Bm D/A | G6 ||

Verse 1

Bm D/A G6
I can't be - lieve the news to - day,

Bm D/A G6
Oh, I can't close my eyes and make it go away

D
How long,

Em7
How long must we sing this song?

D Em7
How long, how long?

Bridge 1

(Em7) Bm* D*
'Cause to - night,

G Bm* D* G
We can be as one to - night.

Verse 2

Bm* D* G
Broken bottles under children's feet,

Bm D/A G6
Bodies strewn across the dead end street.

Bm D/A G6
But I won't heed the battle call,

Bm D/A
It puts my back up,

G6
Puts my back up against the wall.

Chorus 1

```
Bm          D/A          G6
   Sunday,     bloody Sunday,
Bm          D/A          G6
   Sunday,     bloody Sunday.
F           Em7          D        F  Em7  D
   Sunday,     bloody Sunday,
```

Alright lets go!

Link 1

```
| Bm*  D* | G        | Bm*  D* | G        ||
```

Verse 3

```
Bm*          D*                  G
   And the battle's just be - gun,
Bm                    D/A                G6
   There's many lost, but tell me who has won?
Bm                    D/A              G6
   The trench is dug within our hearts,
Bm                    D/A                      G6
   And mothers, children, brothers, sisters torn apart.
Bm          D/A          G6
   Sunday,     bloody Sunday,
Bm          D/A          G6
   Sunday,     bloody Sunday.
D
   How long,
Em7
How long must we sing this song?
D                      Em7
   How long, how long?
```

Bridge 2

```
(Em7)          Bm*     D*
'Cause to - night,
G                            Bm*     D*  G
We can be as one to - night.
     Bm*
To - night.
```

Chorus 2

```
Bm*         D*           G
   Sunday,     bloody Sunday,
Bm*         D*           G
   Sunday,     bloody Sunday.
```

Solo ‖: Bm* D* | G | Bm* D* | G :‖

```
Bm*  D*  G              Bm*                    D*    G
                 Wipe the tears from your eyes,
                Bm*        D*    G
Wipe your tears away.
                 Bm*        D*    G
I wipe your tears away,
                 Bm*        D*    G
I wipe your tears away.
Bm*         D*          G
   (Sunday,    bloody Sunday.)
Bm*         D*          G
   (Sunday,    bloody Sunday.)
```

Bridge 3

```
F             Em7          D                                      F    Em7   D
   Sunday,       bloody Sunday. (Sunday, bloody Sun - day.)
F             Em7          D                                      F    Em7   D
   Sunday,       bloody Sunday. (Sunday, bloody Sun - day.)
```

Link 2 | Bm* D* | G | Bm* D* | G ‖

Verse 4

```
Bm*         D*                      G
   And it's true we are im - mune,
Bm*               D*               G
   When fact is fiction and T. - V. reality.
Bm*                  D*         G
   And today the millions cry,
Bm*              D*                    G
   We eat and drink while to - morrow they die.
Bm*          D*               G
   The real battle yet be - gun
Bm*                D*              G
   To claim the victory Jesus won on...
Bm*          D*             G
   Sunday    bloody Sunday.
Bm*          D*             G        D*
   Sunday    bloody Sunday.
```

Sweet Thing

Words & Music by Van Morrison

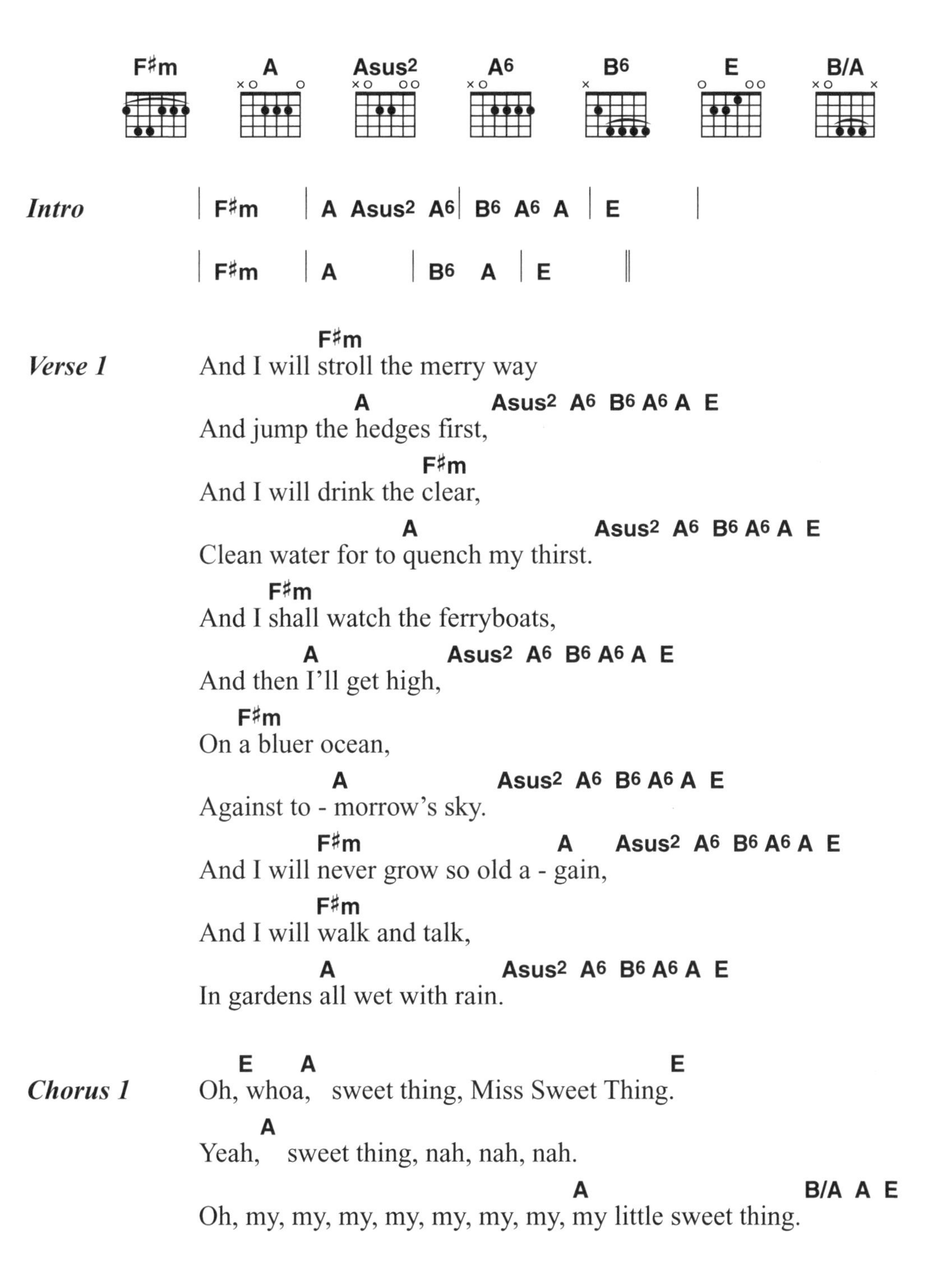

Verse 2

```
              F♯m
And I shall drive my chariot
A                      Asus2  A6  B6  A6 A  E
Down your streets and cry:
       F♯m                      A
"Well,   it's me, I'm dyna - mite
        Asus2                A6  B6 A6 A  E
And I don't know why"
            F♯m
And you shall take me strongly
          A      Asus2        A6  B6 A6  A  E
In your arms           again,
F♯m
   And I wonder if I'll remember
A                      Asus2  A6  B6 A6  A  E
That I ever felt the pain.
            F♯m
We shall walk and talk
                 A                     Asus2                A6  B6 A6 A  E
In gardens all misty and wet, all misty and wet with rain.
      F♯m                    A                 Asus2  A6  B6 A6 A  E
And I will never, never, never grow so old a - gain.
```

Chorus 2

```
    E        A                      E
Oh,   whoa,    you sweet thing.
                     A                                  E
Oh whoa, whoa, you sweet thing, you sweet thing.
                                               A
My, my, my, my, my, my, my, my, my,
                Asus2 A6  B6 A6 A E
my, my, my,
```

```
                    F♯m
Verse 3    And I will raise my hand up
           A                  Asus2  A6  B6  A6 A  E
           Into the night time    sky,
           F♯m
                 And count the stars
           A                   Asus2   A6  B6 A6 A  E
           That's shining in your eye.
                F♯m                         A
           Ah, just to dig it all and not to wonder,
           Asus2                A6  B6 A6  A  E
           That's just fine.
                     F♯m
           And I'll be satisfied
                    A              Asus2      A6  B6 A6  A  E
           Not to read in be - tween the lines.
                F♯m
           And I will walk and talk
              A                          Asus2  A6  B6 A6 A  E
           In gardens all wet with rain,
                         F♯m
           And I will never, ever, ever, ever
           A                     Asus2  A6  B6 A6 A  E
           Grow so old a - gain.

                E       A                    A6   E
Chorus 3   Oh, whoa,     sweet thing.
                                 A                 E
           Oh, whoa, whoa,      sugar baby.
                         A                  E
           Oh, whoa,      sweet thing.
                             A                         E
           Sugar -  baby,      sugar baby, sugar ba - by.
           A                                  E
              With your champagne eyes,
                                      A       E
           And your saint like smile.

           To fade
```

The Time Is Now

Words & Music by Mark Brydon & Róisín Murphy

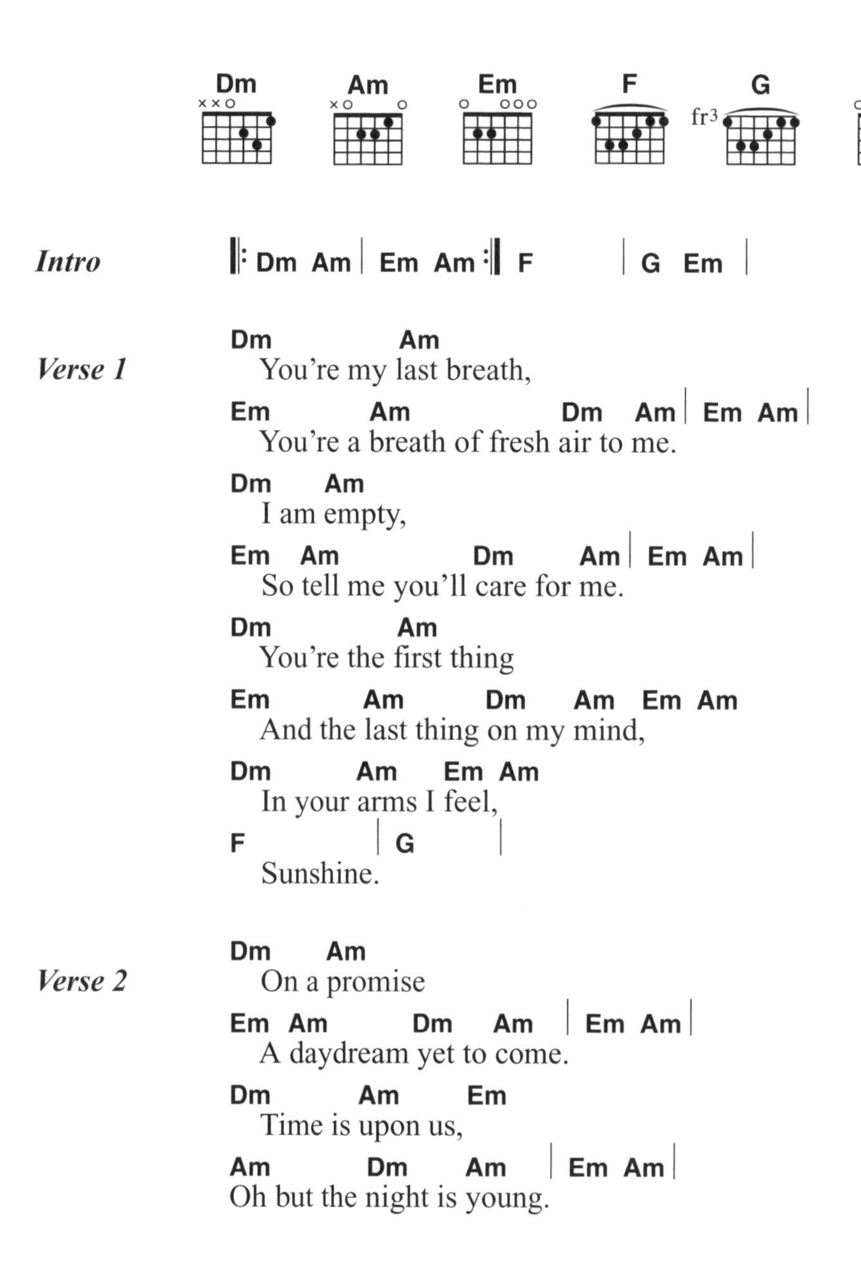


```
Intro     ||: Dm  Am | Em  Am :|| F        | G  Em |

          Dm           Am
Verse 1     You're my last breath,
          Em          Am                Dm   Am | Em Am |
            You're a breath of fresh air to me.
          Dm      Am
            I am empty,
          Em   Am            Dm      Am | Em  Am |
            So tell me you'll care for me.
          Dm           Am
            You're the first thing
          Em          Am        Dm      Am   Em  Am
            And the last thing on my mind,
          Dm        Am     Em  Am
            In your arms I feel,
          F            | G        |
            Sunshine.

          Dm      Am
Verse 2     On a promise
          Em  Am         Dm      Am   | Em  Am |
            A daydream yet to come.
          Dm        Am       Em
            Time is upon us,
          Am           Dm       Am   | Em  Am |
          Oh but the night is young.
```

cont.

```
Dm          Am     Em
   Flowers blossom
Am       Dm     Am   Em  Am
   In the winter time.
Dm         Am      Em  Am
   In your arms I feel
F             | G         |
   Sunshine.
```

Chorus 1

```
Dm                  Am             Em          Am
   Give up your - self unto the moment,
Dm     Am            Em  F
   The time is now.
Dm                  Am             Em          Am
   Give up your - self unto the moment,
F                   G
   Let's make this moment last.
```

Verse 3

```
Dm           Am             Em  Am
   You may find yourself,
Dm           Am             Em  Am
   Out on a limb for me,
Dm          Am            Em  Am
   But you accept is as
F               G
   Part of your destiny.
Dm  Am     Em  Am
      I give all I have,
Dm  Am       Em  Am
      But it's not  e - nough,
Dm  Am        Em        Am
      And my patience I tried
F         G
   So I'm calling your bluff.
```

Chorus 2 As Chorus 1

Chorus 3 As Chorus 1

Middle

```
Dm          E
   And we gave it time,
               Am
All eyes are on the clock,
Dm             Am
   Time takes too much time,
E                       Am         | Dm  Am
   Please make the waiting stop.
          E             Am         | Dm  Am
And the atmosphere is charged,
         E        Am | Dm  Am
And in you I trust,
        E          Am
And I feel no fear as I
F     G
   Do as I must.
```

Chorus 4 As Chorus 1

Verse 4

```
Dm  Am             Em    Am
      Tempted by fate,
Dm    Am     Em    Am
   And I won't hesi - tate,
Dm    Am    Em   Am
   The time is now,
F                     G
   Let's make this moment last.
               Dm    Am | Em  Am |
(I'm not in love.)
Dm    Am    Em    Am | Dm  Am | Em  Am |
   The time is now
F                     G
   Let's make this moment last.
```

Chorus 5

```
Dm                 Am            Em        Am
   Give up your - self unto the moment,
Dm    Am    Em   F
   The time is now.
Dm                 Am            Em        Am
   Give up your - self unto the moment,
F                     G
   Let's make this moment,
Am
Last.
```

Tattoo'd Lady

Words & Music by Rory Gallagher

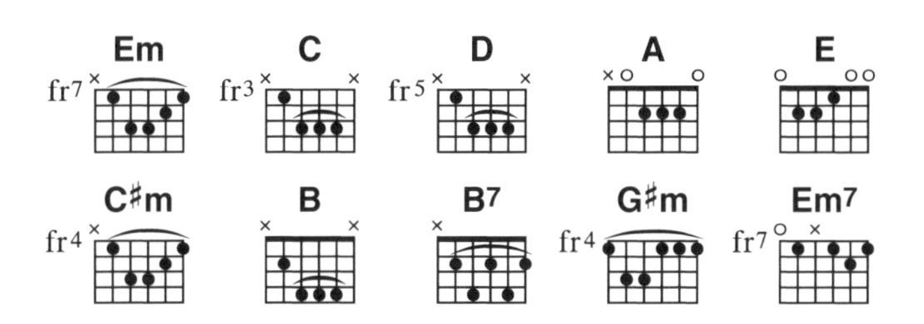

Intro | *Sound fx* ||

Verse 1

```
Em                C                     D                 Em
Tattoo'd lady,    bearded baby, they're my fami - ly.
                       C                            D                   Em
When I was lonely,     something told me, where I could always be.

Where I could push the penny,
C                           D                                Em
If you got any, you'll meet me down at the shooting galle - ry.

Yes, I'm a fairground baby,
C                              D                     Em
   Wonder what made me, fall for the Pearly Queen.
```

Chorus 1

```
        A                          E
Well I spent my youth, under canvas roof,
                          C♯m      B   E
As I roamed from town to town.
         A                        E
I'm not fooling, when I say I got no schoolin',
C♯m                          B7
Never got the school bell sound.
        A                            C♯m
From inside the caravan, I hear the fairground band,
G♯m                          B
Sounding good as they can be.
              A                        C♯m
You know I can't be found, if you look around,
G♯m                              B
Tomorrow we'll be gone by dawn, all right.
```

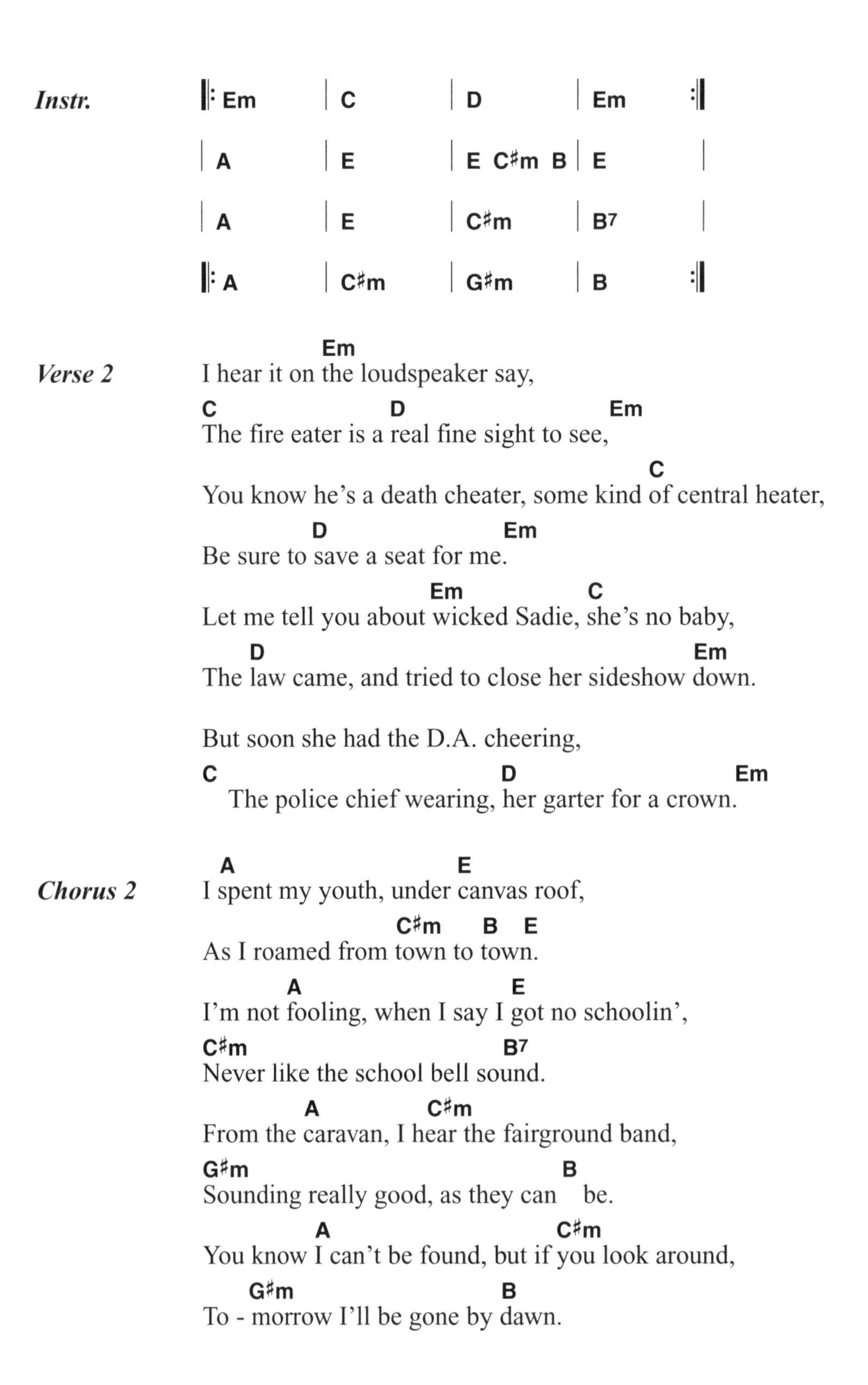

Instr.

:Em	C	D	Em :
A	E	E C♯m B	E
A	E	C♯m	B7
:A	C♯m	G♯m	B :

Verse 2

Em
I hear it on the loudspeaker say,
C D Em
The fire eater is a real fine sight to see,
C
You know he's a death cheater, some kind of central heater,
D Em
Be sure to save a seat for me.
Em C
Let me tell you about wicked Sadie, she's no baby,
D Em
The law came, and tried to close her sideshow down.

But soon she had the D.A. cheering,
C D Em
The police chief wearing, her garter for a crown.

Chorus 2

A E
I spent my youth, under canvas roof,
C♯m B E
As I roamed from town to town.
A E
I'm not fooling, when I say I got no schoolin',
C♯m B7
Never like the school bell sound.
A C♯m
From the caravan, I hear the fairground band,
G♯m B
Sounding really good, as they can be.
A C♯m
You know I can't be found, but if you look around,
G♯m B
To - morrow I'll be gone by dawn.

```
            Em              C               D                    Em
Verse 3     Tattoo'd lady, bearded baby, they're my family.

                                  C
            When I was lonely,    something told me,

                    D               Em
            Where I could always be.

            Where I could push the penny,
            C                                  D                              Em
            If we had any, you'd meet me down, at the shooting gallery.

            Tattoo'd lady!
                                                  Play 12 times
Outro       ||: Em       | C        | D        | Em      :|| Em7          ||
```

Teenage Kicks

Words & Music by John O'Neill

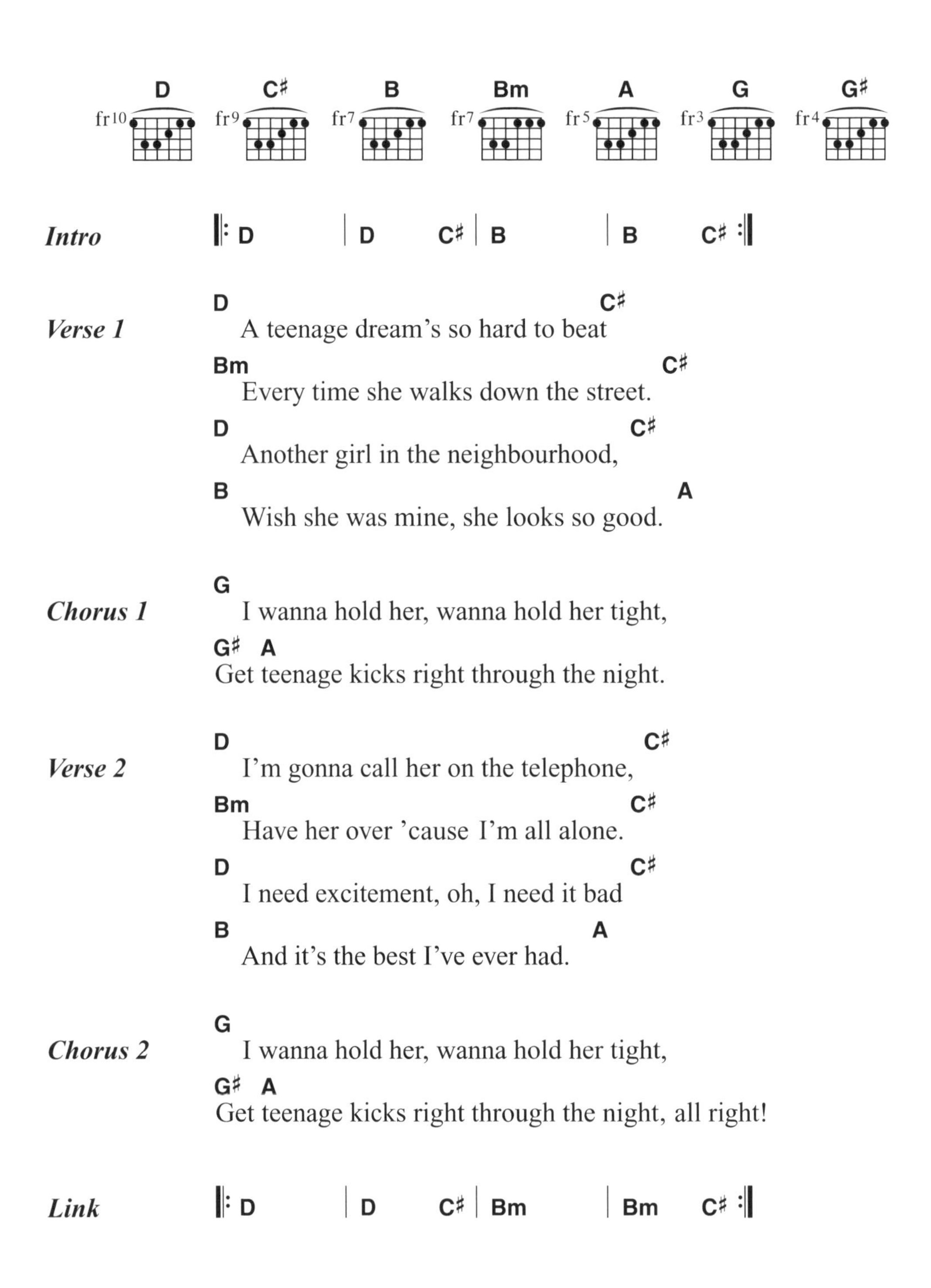

Intro ‖: D | D C♯ | B | B C♯ :‖

Verse 1

D C♯
A teenage dream's so hard to beat
Bm C♯
Every time she walks down the street.
D C♯
Another girl in the neighbourhood,
B A
Wish she was mine, she looks so good.

Chorus 1

G
I wanna hold her, wanna hold her tight,
G♯ A
Get teenage kicks right through the night.

Verse 2

D C♯
I'm gonna call her on the telephone,
Bm C♯
Have her over 'cause I'm all alone.
D C♯
I need excitement, oh, I need it bad
B A
And it's the best I've ever had.

Chorus 2

G
I wanna hold her, wanna hold her tight,
G♯ A
Get teenage kicks right through the night, all right!

Link ‖: D | D C♯ | Bm | Bm C♯ :‖

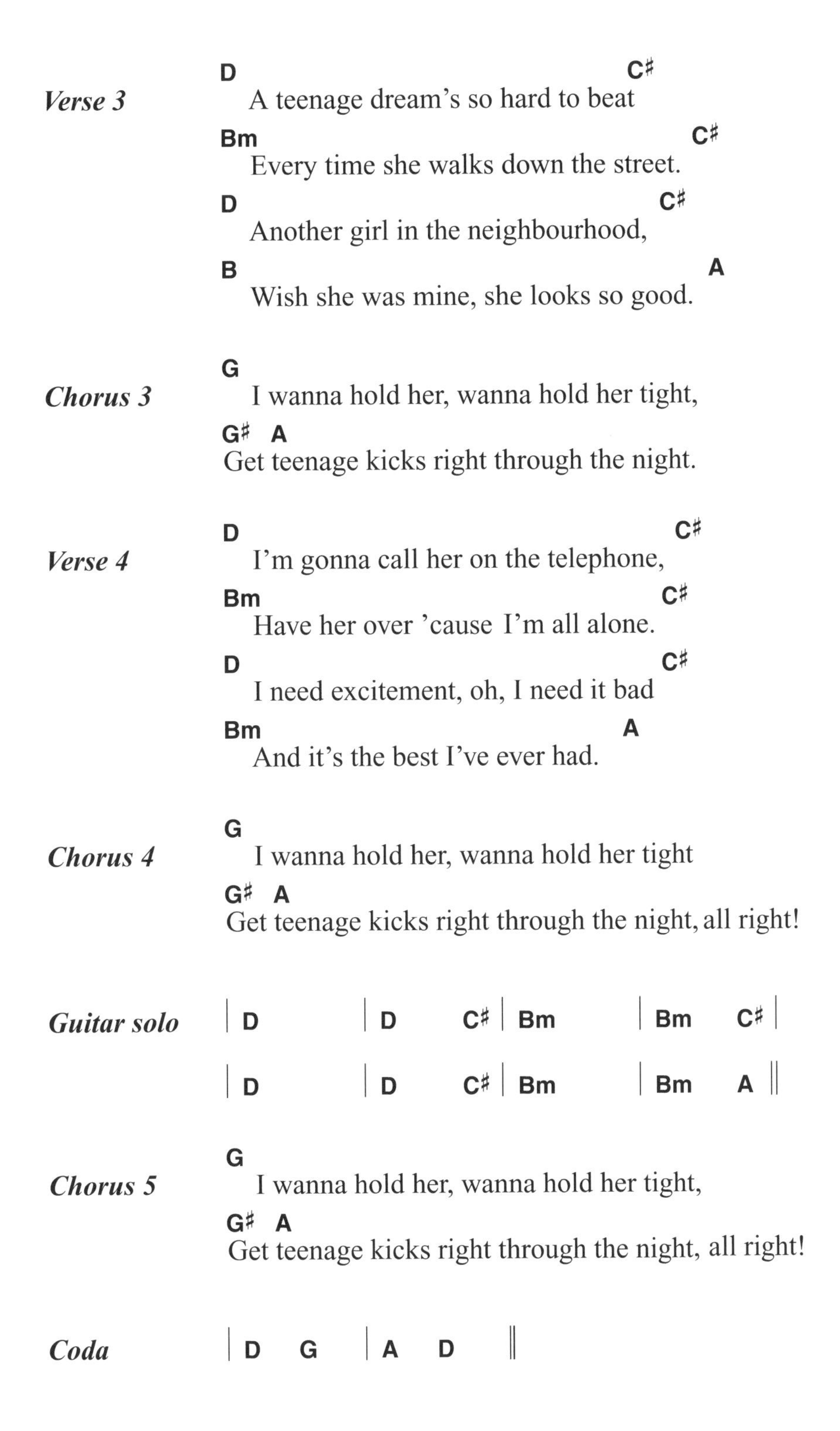

Verse 3

D C♯
A teenage dream's so hard to beat
Bm C♯
Every time she walks down the street.
D C♯
Another girl in the neighbourhood,
B A
Wish she was mine, she looks so good.

Chorus 3

G
I wanna hold her, wanna hold her tight,
G♯ A
Get teenage kicks right through the night.

Verse 4

D C♯
I'm gonna call her on the telephone,
Bm C♯
Have her over 'cause I'm all alone.
D C♯
I need excitement, oh, I need it bad
Bm A
And it's the best I've ever had.

Chorus 4

G
I wanna hold her, wanna hold her tight
G♯ A
Get teenage kicks right through the night, all right!

Guitar solo

| D | D C♯ | Bm | Bm C♯ |
| D | D C♯ | Bm | Bm A ||

Chorus 5

G
I wanna hold her, wanna hold her tight,
G♯ A
Get teenage kicks right through the night, all right!

Coda

| D G | A D ||

To You I Bestow

Words & Music by Edmund Enright

F♯m D D(add9) Esus2/D A Bm E C

Verse 1

F♯m
Wait a minute now, see me when you come back,
D D(add9) Esus2/D
I could be sharing someone else's pillow.
F♯m
And my love for you is better than diamonds,
D D(add9) Esus2/D
To you, everything I be - stow.

Verse 2

F♯m
And to - morrow, I'll be dancin' on my own,
D D(add9) Esus2/D
And I'll need a kiss for my head that's achin'.
F♯m
And I'll be a hungry dog without a bone,
D D(add9) Esus2/D
Hoping my place with you's not taken.

Chorus 1

A Bm D
Kiss me and tell me it's not bro - ken,
A Bm D
Kiss me and kiss me till I'm dead.
A Bm D
See, I give you the stars from the bruised evening sky,
E F♯m
And a crown of jewels for your head now.
D D(add9) Esus2/D
For your head now,
F♯m
For your head now,
D D(add9) Esus2/D
For your head.

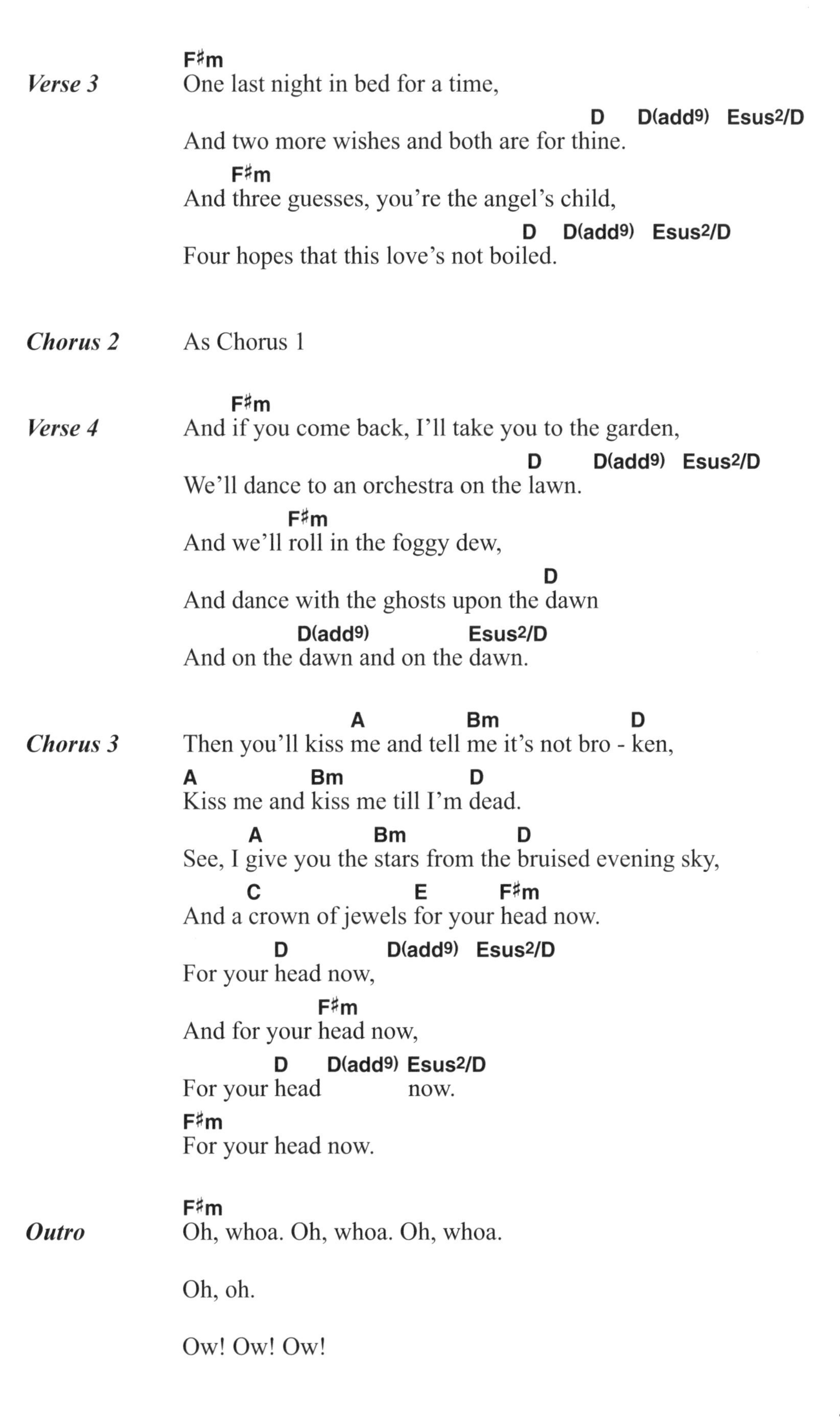

Verse 3

F♯m
One last night in bed for a time,
D D(add9) Esus2/D
And two more wishes and both are for thine.
F♯m
And three guesses, you're the angel's child,
D D(add9) Esus2/D
Four hopes that this love's not boiled.

Chorus 2

As Chorus 1

Verse 4

F♯m
And if you come back, I'll take you to the garden,
D D(add9) Esus2/D
We'll dance to an orchestra on the lawn.
F♯m
And we'll roll in the foggy dew,
D
And dance with the ghosts upon the dawn
D(add9) Esus2/D
And on the dawn and on the dawn.

Chorus 3

A Bm D
Then you'll kiss me and tell me it's not bro - ken,
A Bm D
Kiss me and kiss me till I'm dead.
A Bm D
See, I give you the stars from the bruised evening sky,
C E F♯m
And a crown of jewels for your head now.
D D(add9) Esus2/D
For your head now,
F♯m
And for your head now,
D D(add9) Esus2/D
For your head now.
F♯m
For your head now.

Outro

F♯m
Oh, whoa. Oh, whoa. Oh, whoa.

Oh, oh.

Ow! Ow! Ow!

Whiskey In The Jar

Traditional
Arranged by Phil Lynott, Brian Downey & Eric Bell

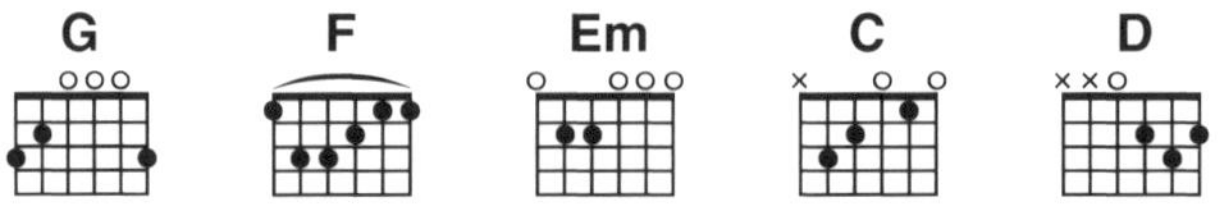

G F Em C D

Intro

| N.C. G F | Em | Em | G | G F |

| Em | Em | G | G |

Verse 1

```
   G                        Em
As I was goin' over the Cork and Kerry mountains
C                          G
I saw Captain Farrell and his money he was countin'.
                               Em
I first produced my pistol and then produced my rapier
      C                        G
I said   stand and deliver or the devil he may take ya.
```

Chorus 1

```
       D
Musha ring dum a doo dum a da
C
   Whack for my daddy-o,

Whack for my daddy-o
       G                     F
There's whiskey in the jar-o.
```

Instrumental

| Em | Em | G | G F | Em | Em | G | G |

Verse 2

```
  G                             Em
I took all of his money and it was a pretty penny
  C                          G
I took all of his money and I brought it home to Molly.
                               Em
She swore that she'd love me, never would she leave me
          C                          G
But the devil take that woman for you know she trick me easy.
```

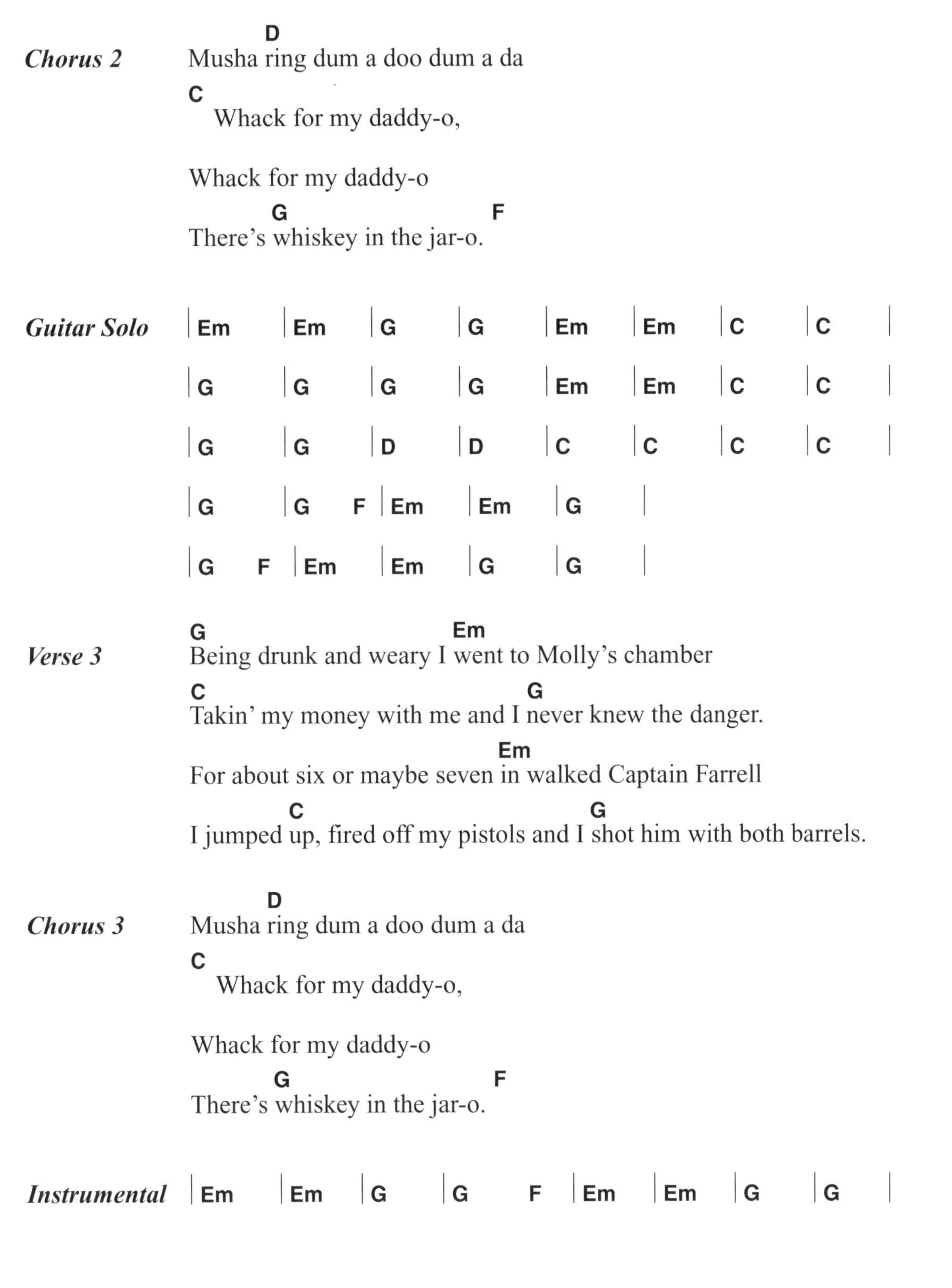

Chorus 2

```
           D
Musha ring dum a doo dum a da
C
   Whack for my daddy-o,

Whack for my daddy-o
          G                        F
There's whiskey in the jar-o.
```

Guitar Solo

Em	Em	G	G	Em	Em	C	C
G	G	G	G	Em	Em	C	C
G	G	D	D	C	C	C	C
G	G F	Em	Em	G
G F	Em	Em	G	G

Verse 3

```
G                             Em
Being drunk and weary I went to Molly's chamber
C                                   G
Takin' my money with me and I never knew the danger.
                                   Em
For about six or maybe seven in walked Captain Farrell
           C                              G
I jumped up, fired off my pistols and I shot him with both barrels.
```

Chorus 3

```
           D
Musha ring dum a doo dum a da
C
   Whack for my daddy-o,

Whack for my daddy-o
          G                        F
There's whiskey in the jar-o.
```

Instrumental | Em | Em | G | G F | Em | Em | G | G |

```
              G                                       Em
*Verse 4*     Now some men like the fishin' and some men like the fowlin'
               C                             G
              And some men like to hear a cannon ball a roarin',
                          Em
              Me I like sleepin' especially in my Molly's chamber
               C                               G
              But here I am in prison, here I am with a ball and chain, yeah.

                   D
*Chorus 4*    Musha ring dum a doo dum a da
              C
                Whack for my daddy-o,

              Whack for my daddy-o
                    G                 F
              There's whiskey in the jar-o.

*Outro*       ||: Em    | Em    | G     | G    F :||       Repeat to fade
```

The World Is What You Make It

Words & Music by Paul Brady

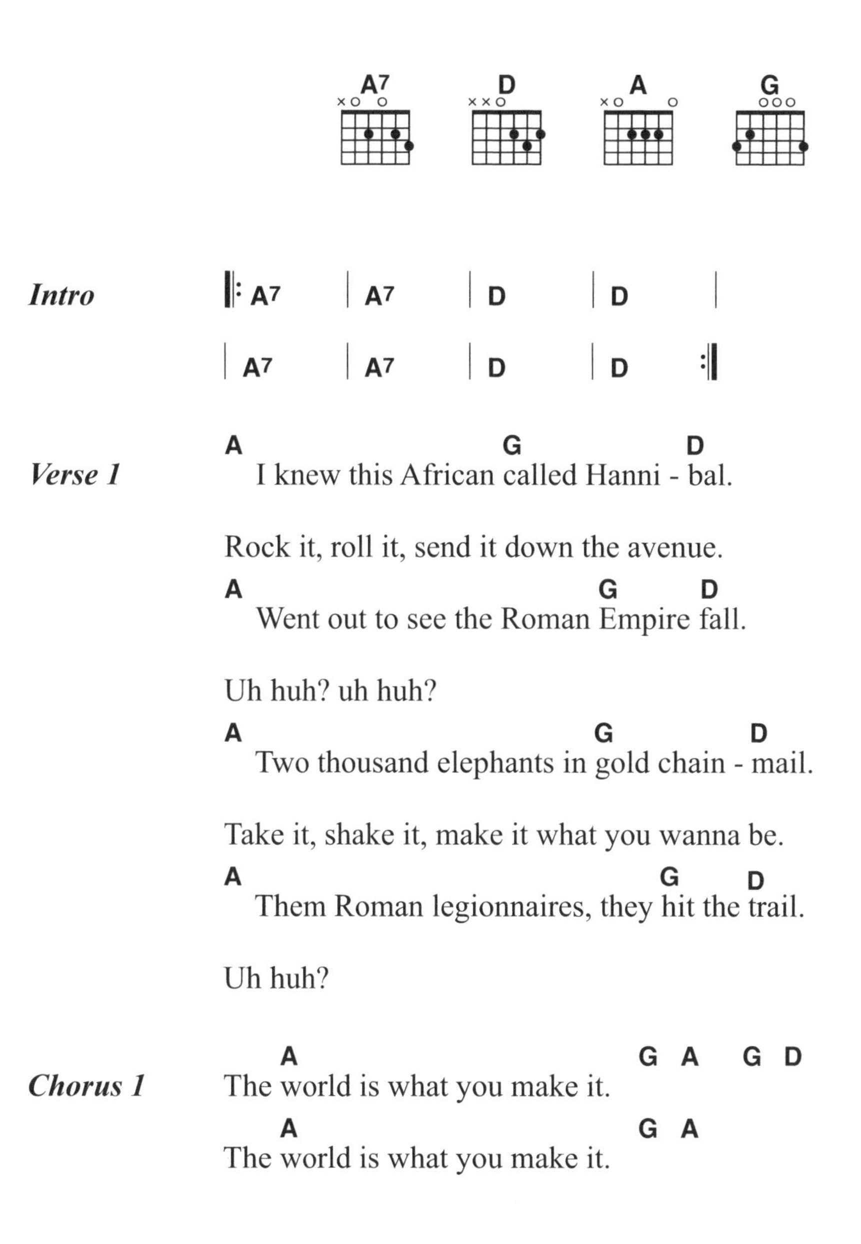

Intro

|: A7 | A7 | D | D |

| A7 | A7 | D | D :|

Verse 1

A G D
I knew this African called Hanni - bal.

Rock it, roll it, send it down the avenue.

A G D
Went out to see the Roman Empire fall.

Uh huh? uh huh?

A G D
Two thousand elephants in gold chain - mail.

Take it, shake it, make it what you wanna be.

A G D
Them Roman legionnaires, they hit the trail.

Uh huh?

Chorus 1

A G A G D
The world is what you make it.

A G A
The world is what you make it.

```
          A                             G      D
Verse 2     When Cleopatra lived in Egypt's land.

          Jump down, turn around, look at what the monkey did.
          A                               G      D
            She went to find herself a mighty man.

          Uh huh? uh huh?
          A                          G   D
            In come Antonio from Ita - ly.

          Haul it, ball it, drag it up the pyramid.
          A                               G          D
            He never knew how hot a girl could be.

          Uh huh?

                A                              G  A
Chorus 2  The world is what you make it.
                                             G  D
          The world is what you make it ba - by.
                A                              G  A
          The world is what you make it.

Link 1    | A       | G  A    | A       | G  D    |

          | A       | G  A    | A       | A       ||

          A                                      D
Bridge 1    La, la, la, la, la, la, la, la, la, la, la.

          Oh, da, da, da, do, la, la, la.
          A                                      D
            La, la, la, la, la, la, la, la, la, la, la.
          A                                      D
            La, la, la, la, la, la, la, la, la, la, la.

          La, la, da, da, da ldo, la, la, la.
          A                                      D
            La, la, la, la, la, la, la, la, la, la, la.
```

Verse 3

(A)
Don't start to hit me with your no can do.

Bluesin', losin', workin' up an attitude.

Clean up them windows, let the sun shine through.

Uh huh? uh huh?

A G D
There ain't no happy time with - out no pain.

Heartbreak, new date, move on up the alleyway.

A G D
Pick up them pieces hit the road a - gain.

Uh huh?

Chorus 3 As Chorus 2

Bridge 2 As Bridge 1

Bridge 3

A D
La, la, la, la, la, la, la, la, la, la, la.

Oh, da, da, da do, la, la, la.

A D
La, la, la, la, la, la, la, la, la, la, la.

Chorus 4 As Chorus 2

Link 2 As Link 1

Chorus 5 As Chorus 2

You Raise Me Up

Words & Music by Rolf Løvland & Brendan Graham

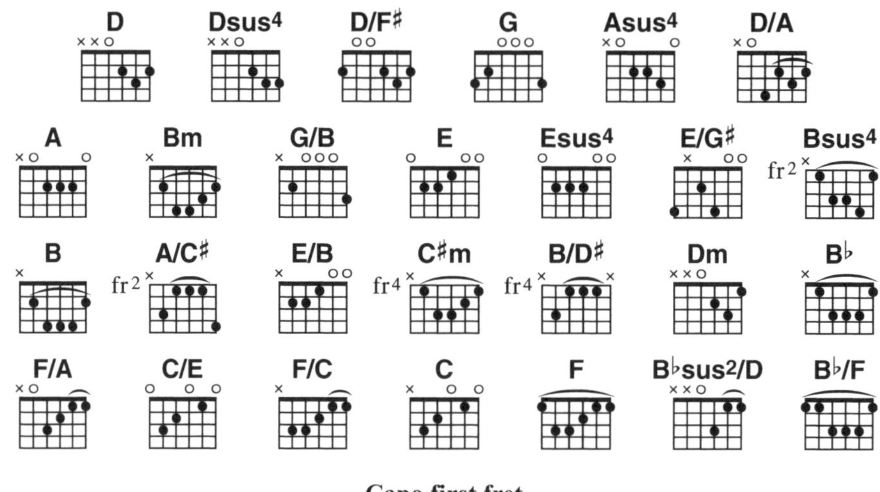

Capo first fret

Intro | **D** | **D** ‖

Verse 1

D **Dsus4** **D**
When I am down and oh my soul, so weary,
D/F♯ **G** **Asus4**
When troubles come and my heart burdened be,
G **D**
Then I am still and wait here in the silence,
G **D/A** **A** **D**
Until you come and sit a while with me.

Chorus 1

(D) **Bm** **G** **D/F♯** **A**
You raise me up so I can stand on mountains,
Bm **G** **D/F♯** **A**
You raise me up to walk on stormy seas.
D **G/B** **D/A** **D/F♯** **A**
I am strong when I am on your shoul - ders,
D/A **A** **D**
You raise me up to more than I can be.

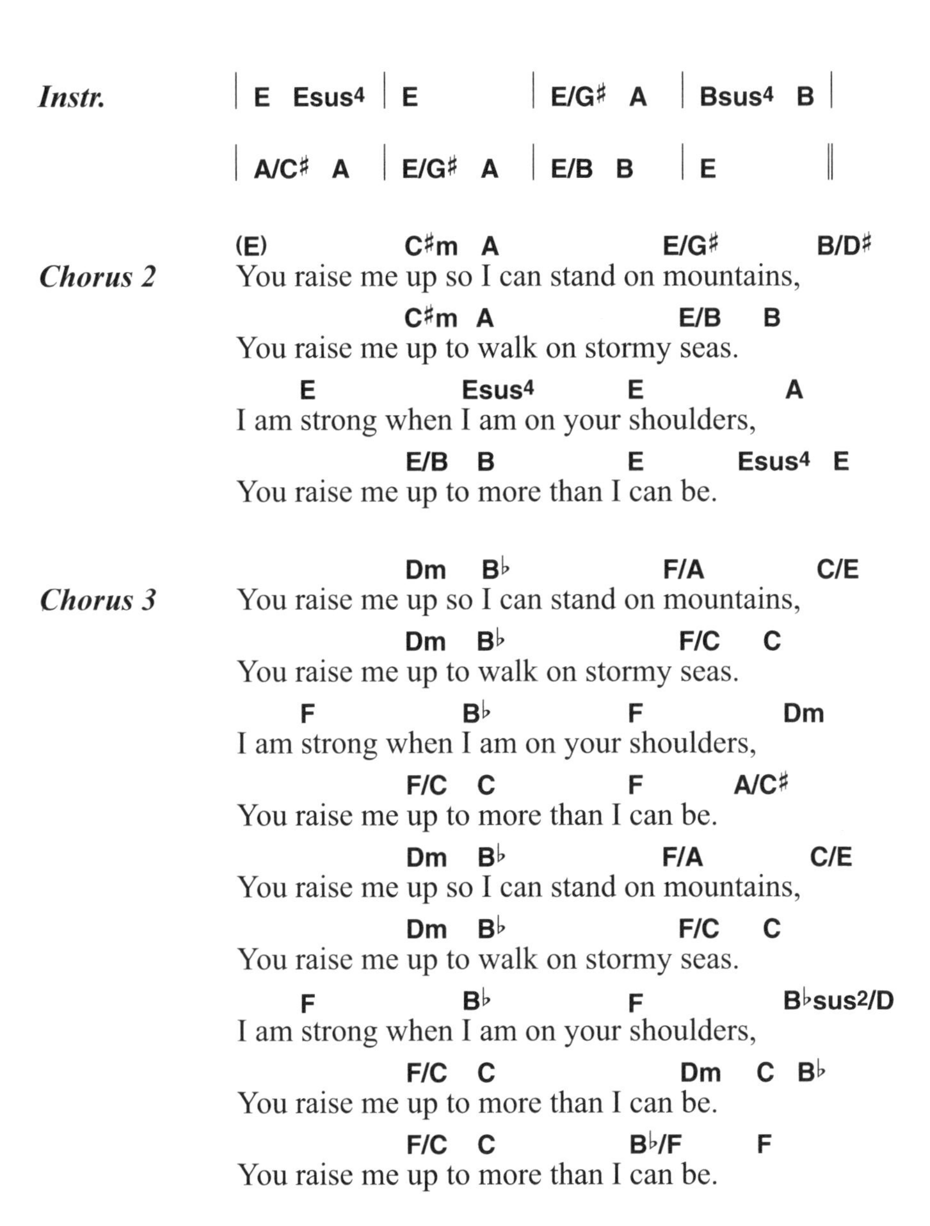

```
Instr.      | E   Esus4 | E         | E/G♯  A   | Bsus4  B  |

            | A/C♯  A   | E/G♯  A   | E/B  B    | E         ‖

            (E)             C♯m  A                E/G♯          B/D♯
Chorus 2    You raise me up so I can stand on mountains,
                            C♯m  A                  E/B   B
            You raise me up to walk on stormy seas.
                  E              Esus4           E             A
            I am strong when I am on your shoulders,
                            E/B   B              E          Esus4   E
            You raise me up to more than I can be.


                            Dm    B♭                F/A           C/E
Chorus 3    You raise me up so I can stand on mountains,
                            Dm    B♭                  F/C    C
            You raise me up to walk on stormy seas.
                  F              B♭              F              Dm
            I am strong when I am on your shoulders,
                            F/C   C              F          A/C♯
            You raise me up to more than I can be.
                            Dm    B♭                F/A          C/E
            You raise me up so I can stand on mountains,
                            Dm    B♭                  F/C    C
            You raise me up to walk on stormy seas.
                  F              B♭              F              B♭sus2/D
            I am strong when I am on your shoulders,
                            F/C   C                   Dm     C   B♭
            You raise me up to more than I can be.
                            F/C   C              B♭/F         F
            You raise me up to more than I can be.
```

Your Pretty Smile

Words & Music by Damien Dempsey

Cmaj7 Em C G D D7 Am7 Am

Capo first fret

Intro

```
N.C.
Mmm, your pretty smile banish any gloom.

║: Cmaj7 | Em | Cmaj7 | Em :║
```

Verse 1

```
Em          C                G                D
And when I frown I feel un - sound, I drag you down to ground level.
Em        C                  G                D
   I inter - rupt your flying high and summer sky in your mind.
Em               C              G                D
   But then you grab me by the scruff and we're up, up and over,
Em           C         G                D                D7
   Over the dirty mental streets where I re - treat from living.
```

Chorus 1

```
G                         C
Your pretty smile it could light up any room,
G                      C
I've seen it many times banish any gloom.
D                 Am7                D             Am7
Darlin', don't you ever stop with that smilin', yeah.
G                         C
Your pretty smile it could light up any room,
G                      C
I've seen it many times banish any gloom.
D                 Am7                D             Am7
Darlin', don't you ever stop with that smilin', yeah.
```

Verse 2

```
Em          C                 G                D
One time I seen the golden screen, I was six - teen and spellbound,
Em          C                 G          D
   I think of you when I glance over these old reels.
Em            C                 G                D
   Greta Gar - bo, Brigitte Bar - dot, Marilyn Mon - roe, such photo's.
Em                C                  G           D        D7
   The smog des -cends around my    silhouette of dreams.
```

Chorus 2 As Chorus 1

Instr. | Cmaj7 | Em | Cmaj7 | Em ||

Bridge

```
Cmaj7         Em
   Baby, baby,    baby, baby.
Cmaj7         Em
   Baby, baby,    baby.
     G          C             G            C   D7     Am  D7  Am
Baby your pretty smile it could light up most any room.
     G          C             G            C   D7     Am  D7  Am
I said your pretty smile it could light up most any room.
     G          C             G            C   D7     Am  D7  Am
I said your pretty smile it could light up most any room.
```

Outro

```
     G
Your pretty smile,
     C               G            C        D7  Am  D7  Am
Your pretty smile could light up most any room.
     G
Your pretty smile,
     C               G            C        D7  Am  D7  Am
Your pretty smile could light up most any room.
     G
Your pretty smile,
     C               G            C        D7  Am  D7  Am
Your pretty smile could light up most any room.
```

To fade

You Made Me The Thief Of Your Heart

Words & Music by Gavin Friday, Paul Hewson & Morris Roycroft

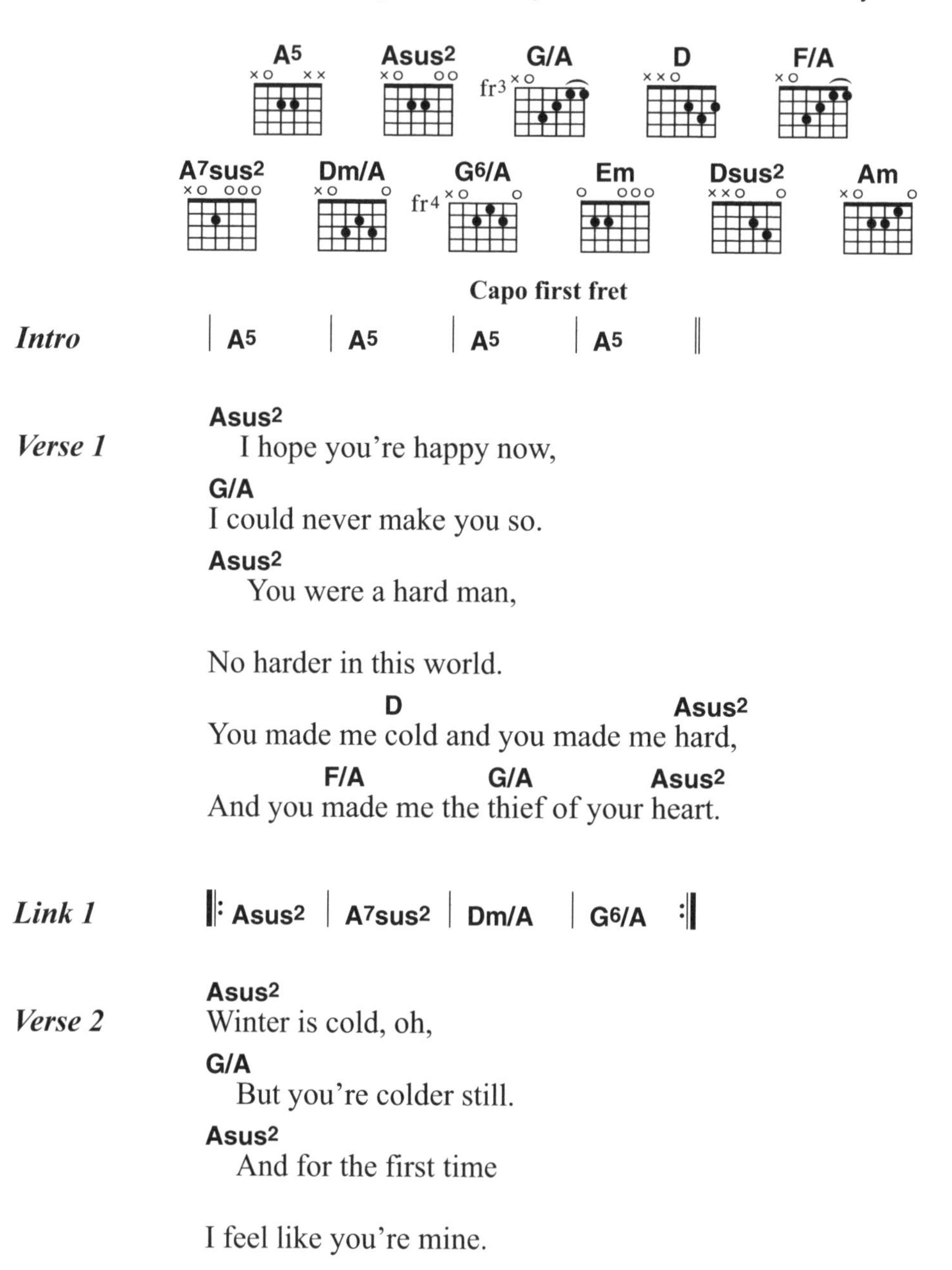

Capo first fret

Intro | A5 | A5 | A5 | A5 ||

Verse 1

```
Asus2
   I hope you're happy now,
G/A
I could never make you so.
Asus2
    You were a hard man,

No harder in this world.
                 D                      Asus2
You made me cold and you made me hard,
               F/A           G/A          Asus2
And you made me the thief of your heart.
```

Link 1 ||: Asus2 | A7sus2 | Dm/A | G6/A :||

Verse 2

```
Asus2
Winter is cold, oh,
G/A
   But you're colder still.
Asus2
   And for the first time

I feel like you're mine.
```

```
                      D
cont.       I'll share you with the one
                                     Asus2
            Who will mend what falls a - part,
               F/A          G/A
            And turn a blind eye
                 Em           Asus2
            To the thief of your heart.


Link 2      |: Asus2 | A7sus2 | Dm/A  | G6/A :|

            | Asus2  | D      | Asus2 | Dm/A  |

            | Asus2  | F/A    | Dsus2 ||

              Am
Chorus 1    Oh,   you lost,

            Oh, you lost all.

            You lost all,

            You lost all.

            Asus2       A7sus2
Verse 3       I'll never wash these clothes,
            Dm/A
              I want to keep the stain.
            Asus2              A7sus2
              Your blood to me is precious,
            Dm/A
              Nor would I spill it in vain.
            Asus2       D
              Your spirit sings,
                        G/A        Am
            Though your lips never part.
                    F/A     G/A
            Singing only to me,
               Em          Asus2
            The thief of your heart.
```

Link 3

| : Asus2 | A7sus2 | Dm/A | G6/A : |

| Asus2 | D | Asus2 | Dm/A |

| Asus2 | F/A | Dsus2 ||

| : Am | Am | Am | Am : |

Link 4

| : Asus2 | A7sus2 | Dm/A | G6/A : |

| Asus2 | D | Asus2 | Dm/A |

| Asus2 | F/A | Dsus2 |

Am
Oh, you lost.

Instr.

| : Am | Am | Am | Am : |

Outro

Am
Oh, you lost,

Oh, you lost all,

Lost all.

Oh, you lost,

Oh, you lost all,

Lost all. *To fade*

1 2 3 4 5 6 7 8 9